TRUE - LIFE SCOTTISH CRIME CAPERS

INSPECTOR ARCHIE
MURDOCH
INVESTIGATES

Best wishes to Bill MacPherson

Bob Beveridge

BY

BOB BEVERIDGE

LANG SYNE PUBLISHERS LTD.
GLASGOW

INSPECTOR ARCHIE MURDOCH INVESTIGATES

Inspector Archie Murdoch Investigates was
published in 1995 by Lang Syne Publishers Ltd.
Clydeway Centre, 45 Finnieston Street, Glasgow, G3 8JU
Printed by Waterside Printers. Cover Illustration by Andy Wilson.
Design by Andrew Morgan. ©Bob Beveridge 1995
ISBN 185217 0174

THE EXPECTED VISIT

Constable George Page had just taken up his first day's duty on the police force, and delivering witness citations was one of the many tedious tasks delegated to rookie policemen.

"It's still a lot mair fun than workin' in a paper mill," commented George to some of his colleagues as he had his first tea break in the police station canteen.

"Aye, ye dinnae meet queer characters in a paper mill like the wan Ah met this morning," continued the young probationary constable.

Inspector Murdoch was sitting at a nearby table in the canteen and his ears cocked up when he overheard this comment.

"Wha's this ye've been runnin' intae?" asked one of the constables.

"Well, Ah had a citation tae deliver tae number 12 Main Street and there was no-one at home so Ah rung the doorbell at number 14 tae see if the neighbour knew where Ah could find the person Ah wis lookin fir," said P.C. Page.

"And whit happened?" queried the impatient Cadet Morgan.

"Well, when this auld man eventually answered the door Ah jokingly said that we'd caught him at last," replied Page. "He made a strange reply and gave me the impression that he had done something sinister in his past."

"What did he say?" queried Morgan.

In response to Constable Page's lighthearted introductory remark, the old man had replied, "Aye, you had better come in. Ah've been expecting ye fir years now."

On hearing this most curious remark, Inspector Murdoch had to intervene. "Did ye ask him what exactly he meant when he said he'd been expecting us?" he asked as he drew his chair alongside P.C. Page. The young constable had not pursued the matter, other than asking the whereabouts of the next door neighbour.

Detective Inspector Murdoch was an experienced officer and his instincts told him that it might be worth paying the strange occupant at 14 Main Street a visit.

"Constable Page," shouted Murdoch, "get yerself oot o' that uniform and intae civilian clothes because yer gaun wi' me on yer first CID assignment."

Unclear situations like this bothered Murdoch and he could not wait to pay the occupant at 14 Main Street a visit and see what skeleton was in the cupboard! It wasn't long before the Inspector and Constable Page in plain clothes were knocking loudly on the door of their quarry. After some persistent banging there was no response but the occupant at number 12 on hearing all the commotion came to his front door to see what was going on.

His name was Donald Brown and he had been the person referred to in the witness citation that Constable Page had been seeking to deliver earlier that day.

"Ye can serve the citation on Mr. Brown noo," said Murdoch to the junior officer.

"Ah cannae dae that, sir," replied P.C. Page, "because Ah've left the citation in ma tunic pocket and that, as ye know, is at the station with the rest o' ma police uniform."

"Och, we'll see tae that later on but in the meantime let's get back tae the matter in hand," said the inspector.

The officers soon learned from Mr. Brown that his neighbour at number 14 was an elderly man called John Paterson.

"He's a guid neebour, Mr. Murdoch," said Brown, "but the only annoying thing is that he maks these loud, banging noises nearly every nicht and the din goes on, often intae the wee sma' hoors o' the morning."

The officers also learned from Brown that the sinister Mr. Paterson was indeed at home and not answering the door.

"Ah seen him jist two meenits before ye arrived," commented the well-meaning neighbour.

Murdoch and Page returned to the door of the flat occupied by the suspect and resumed their loud knocking.

Constable Page was kneeling down and peering through the letter box.

"He's in there richt enough, sir," said Page, "Ah could see him carrying what looks like a holdall across the lobby."

"Will ye answer the door, Mr. Paterson," shouted Murdoch through the letterbox. "This is police business and we ken yir in there."

After some time, a timid, bespectacled old man unlocked the door and admitted the officers.

"Ah'll come straight tae the point, Mr. Paterson," said Murdoch, "we want tae know just exactly what ye meant when ye said you've

4

been expecting a visit from the police fir years?"

The old man hung his head. "You had better hae a look at this," he said as he opened the door to a bedroom.

Murdoch and Page stepped inside and could not believe their eyes.

There were two shilling pieces (florins) everywhere. The shiny new coins were strewn over the bed. The floor, the mantelpiece and a workbench were totally drenched in coins. The room accommodated thousands of coins. The officers, especially Murdoch, had never seen anything like this in their entire service.

"Are ye some kind o' coin collector or jist running a branch o' the Royal Mint?" exclaimed the inspector with his mouth ajar in disbelief at the sight before him. In those days a two shilling piece was worth more than one pound today!

"He's certainly nae coin collector, inspector," said Constable Page who had been examining a handful of the silver florins.

"What makes ye think that?" responded Murdoch.

"All these coins have exactly the same date, 1957," replied Page.

Murdoch delved his way into the vast piles of coins and sure enough all the coins bore the same date.

"But thae coins cannae be fakes. They look absolutely perfect tae me," gasped Murdoch.

The timid Mr. Paterson quietly volunteered that he had been forging coins for many years. He showed the flabbergasted officers the press, dies and special equipment that he used for the purpose. The noise late at nights, which the neighbour had mentioned, was made by Paterson churning out his fake coins by the hundred. The suspect was taken into custody and enquiries revealed a remarkable background to this case.

Some 20 years previously, Paterson had been convicted and jailed for a similar offence while he lived in the city. The forger was an experienced and extraordinary metal worker who never ever revealed to anyone his incredible ability to produce at low cost such perfect fakes.

The phoney two shilling pieces were inspected by senior bank officials and representatives of the Royal Mint who came to a remarkable conclusion. These experts in money production were unable to distinguish between the fake coins made by Paterson and the real coins which emerged from the Royal Mint! The perfect fakes were even produced at a lower cost than the Mint could turn them out.

The cupro-nickel metal used by the forger was also of the best quality. The fake coins are to this day in the police museum and still they baffle examiners who are unable to determine the difference between them and the real coinage. Despite his age, the elderly John Paterson was sent to prison where he died without completing his sentence.

When in jail he was approached by officials from the Royal Mint who offered all sorts of incentives for him to reveal his secret of being able to make these coins at a price lower than the official government body. Paterson refused to co-operate and took his secret to the grave.

Some years later a young police officer unearthed a startling discovery which had gone un-noticed by the authorities and experts. Florins (or two shilling bits) had serrated nicks round their edge. In the fakes produced by Paterson there was just one nick less than those found on the originals!

Constable Page in his first tour of duty had solved one of Scotland's most interesting crimes. Paterson was betrayed by his own guilty conscience and his response to Constable Page's lighthearted comment about the police catching up on him brought this crime to light, a crime which probably would never have been uncovered otherwise.

THE WILY MR. WYLIE

It is amazing the extraordinary lengths some people will go to in order to commit the perfect crime.

There were times during an enquiry when circumstances would unfold and Detective Inspector Murdoch would finish up dealing with a crime which was entirely different from the one he first set out to investigate.

It was this unpredictable outcome that made criminal enquiries so interesting. "A bit like going on a mystery tour," Murdoch would say, "you dinnae know where you're going tae finish up."

Church Lane in the town was a quiet avenue of small houses with walled gardens. One of the houses had been owned for the past eight years by George Mitchell who lived there with his family and the pet labrador dog. Sadly, due to old age the pet dog died and George chose to bury the much cherished animal at the bottom of the garden.

Whilst digging away, George unearthed a black wig and, further into the soil, his spade became entangled in a lady's old-fashioned wine-coloured coat with a distinctive black velvet collar. Rather than make the task of digging more arduous, he by-passed these items and soon the harrowing task of burying the remains of the family pet was complete.

Mitchell thought nothing of the wig and coat and simply left them where they had been buried. Some months later, the Mitchells invited friends and neighbours to a party at their house and during the evening the usual blethering and verbal exchanges took place. It was then that neighbour Ron Evans made a comment which made George Mitchell tremble.

"You know, George, it was a right queer couple that stayed here for a wee while before you," said Evans. "You never saw them together and the wife was only seen on rare occasions driving his van but he was never with her."

"What was queer about them?" enquired George.

"Nobody ever spoke to them and when she was seen driving alone in his van she always wore a black wig and an old fashioned coat with a black velvet collar," said Evans, "and after his wife left him he just moved away."

"The wife left him?" queried George.

"Aye, that was years ago and he reported her missing but she wis never traced," came the chilling response from Evans.

George Mitchell was visibly stunned at this news.

"What's wrang, George? You look like you've seen a ghost," said Evans.

George then explained about the coat and wig he discovered in the garden and then came the obvious question, "Where was the body of the wife?"

The police were immediately alerted and from the missing persons file Detective Inspector Archie Murdoch confirmed that John Wylie, an insurance agent, had reported over seven years ago the disappearance of his wife Susan. She, according to Wylie, just walked out on him and was never seen again.

In the initial report Wylie alleged that his wife was wearing a black collared, wine coat and a black wig when she disappeared.

Seven years passed by and Wylie went to the courts and had his wife declared 'missing - presumed dead'.

This meant he was legally free, if he chose, to remarry, inherit from the spouse's estate or cash any life insurance if indeed there was any.

Inspector Murdoch soon had an entire posse of policemen digging up the Mitchell garden but apart from recovering the coat and wig there was no sign of the remains of ill-fated Mrs. Wylie.

The absence of a body disappointed the inspector but he managed to say, "By jings, Mitchell, this is a crafty way of gettin' yer gairden dug for ye!"

Nobody seemed to know where Wylie had gone, following the wife's disappearing trick but Inspector Murdoch checked the court records and learned that the suspect had an address in Argyllshire.

Enquiries there, however, revealed that Wylie had moved back to Murdoch's area and he was currently staying at a remote cottage, a few miles out of town.

Inspector Murdoch and Detective Constable Soutar obtained a search warrant and they soon headed off in the direction of Wylie's cottage.

It was arranged that two constables would take Wylie to the police station for later questioning whilst his cottage was searched.

During the search, Murdoch was puzzled with the discovery in a desk of several birth certificates, all relating to women, and all roughly in the same age category as Wylie.

"Let's get back to the station, Soutar, and see what chummy-boy's got to say for himself," announced Murdoch. Sometimes an aggressive, straight-to-the-point approach paid dividends and the inspector decided to take this stance when interviewing the suspect.

"Wylie," screeched Murdoch, "the finding of your wife's coat and wig in the garden of your auld hoose proves that your version concerning her disappearance is a complete lie," continued Murdoch. "You've murdered your wife, Mr. Wylie, and I'll prove it, even if it takes me anither seven years."

"I dinnae ken whit yer gettin' all steamed up aboot, sergeant," said Wylie in a calm tone.

"It's Inspector Murdoch, no sergeant," interrupted Soutar.

"It doesn't make ony difference," said Wylie, "because I don't have, and never had, a wife - so how could Ah have murdered her?"

The officers were taken aback by Wylie's account of events.

"Mr. and Mrs. Wylie" were never seen together because the 'wife' was, in fact, Wylie himself, dressed in the coat and wearing the wig. To secure the success of his fraudulent scheme it was necessary that 'she' be seen from time to time.

In his capacity as an insurance agent he was able to take out an insurance policy payable on 'her' death and by keeping the sum involved at a normal level no great suspicion fell on him.

Also, as an agent arranging other people's life insurance it was necessary to acquire their birth certificates and he would hang on to some of these by pretending to his clients that his briefcase containing the documents had been stolen.

He then chose a suitable certificate which enabled him to process the life insurance for his non-existent wife. The same birth certificate was required when he made application to the courts to have his 'wife' presumed dead, thereafter he could cash the life insurance policy. This he had successfully done.

It had been a clever scheme and Wylie was patient enough to wait seven years to secure his illicit reward but the passing of the Mitchell's pet labrador brought about the downfall of Mr. Edward Wylie, insurance agent, the widower who wasn't.

Locking the scoundrel up in the cells, Inspector Murdoch said, "If yer thinking aboot gettin' married again, Mr. Wylie, drop us an invitation!"

WHERE THERE'S A WILL

Sergeant McPherson was on duty at the police station when he received a telephone call from Mr. Simpson who was a lawyer in the town.

"It's a matter of some delicacy," said Mr. Simpson in a whispered tone of voice. "Perhaps you could arrange for plainclothes officers to call at my office."

Later that day Detective Sergeant Lindsay and Detective Constable Soutar called on Mr. Simpson at his place of business. On being invited to take a seat, Sergeant Lindsay wondered how on earth lawyers ever got on with their business because Mr. Simpson's office was littered with piles of books, papers and documents, all bound together with the little pieces of red coloured ribbon tape that solicitors use.

Despite the disarray, Mr. Simpson, fumbling his way through mountains of papers on his desk, soon found the documents he was looking for.

"These two holograph wills, concerning the estate of the late Miss Cook, have come into my possession. Both have apparently or at least appear to have been written by her," said the lawyer, "but one is obviously a forgery. A holograph will is a simple testament written usually on ordinary notepaper and providing the signature is witnessed it's perfectly valid and legal under Scots Law."

He continued to inform the officers that he had been appointed to wind up Miss Cook's affairs as she had no relatives and in the absence of a will the estate would fall to the Crown.

The lawyer's dilemma was that he had two wills allegedly written in Miss Cook's own hand! The first one was genuine as the witnesses were known personally to him and the second one, although witnessed, was obviously an astonishing forgery. It was dated later than the first, bore a close resemblance to Miss Cook's handwriting but the witnesses were not so readily verified as they had both died recently.

The first will had been among Miss Cook's personal effects and the second one had been posted to the lawyer by Mr. John Reid who just happened to be the beneficiary named in this somewhat dubious piece of notepaper. Looking at the two wills, a bewildered Sergeant

Lindsay said, "This is unbelievable, so much so I don't even think we'll need handwriting samples to prove something very strange has been going on!"

The officers took possession of the two wills for further examination and were also given the keys to the late Miss Cook's house by the lawyer.

Enquiries revealed that the named beneficiary in the suspicious will lived close by. John Reid was an unemployed clerk and for a number of years he had kindly helped Miss Cook by doing numerous chores around the house. Miss Cook had trusted him absolutely and being an elderly lady living alone she was most grateful to Reid for the help he had given her.

During the last eight months of her life Miss Cook had been confined in hospital and during this time the quiet, kind Mr. Reid was entrusted to look after her house. Having the keys to the house gave him easy access to Miss Cook's diary and personal papers.

Detective Sergeant Lindsay and Constable Soutar searched Miss Cook's home and found notepaper identical to that on which the second testament was written. While comparing the notepaper, Soutar pointed out to his sergeant that the date on this sceptical will coincided with the time Miss Cook was in hospital.

"Nip round to the hospital straight away, Soutar," said Sergeant Lindsay, "and find out as much as you can about Miss Cook's condition at the time and I'll see you later on at the station."

On his return, Constable Soutar told the sergeant that, due to the very grave nature of Miss Cook's illness at this time, the medical staff at the hospital could testify that Miss Cook could not be the author of the second will.

Because of the bizarre content of the two wills, Sergeant Lindsay thought it would be unnecessary at this stage to consider handwriting samples for comparative analysis and he also ruled out other elementary checks that can be done in case of forgery.

"We'll just take the bull by the horns and go and see this man Reid and see what he's got to say for himself," Sergeant Lindsay said to Soutar.

Reid was a quiet, timid little man who lived alone with his 14-year-old daughter. He had not worked in his job as a clerk since his wife died. When the officers called at his home he courteously invited them in and offered to make some tea. Taking advantage of Reid's timid nature, Sergeant Lindsay produced the suspicious will and growled, "I'm going to get straight to the point, Mr. Reid. Miss

11

Cook never wrote this document - but you did."

Before the accused could reply, the Sergeant raised the tone of his voice even further and blasted, "Don't even think about denying it as this would only be wasting mair of my valuable time and heaven knows I've spent enough of that on this case already."

Guilt was written all over Reid's face and the helpful, mild-mannered little man confessed to forging the will in order to benefit from Miss Cook's estate.

"What possessed you to do this, Mr. Reid. It all seems out of character and you've never been in trouble with the police before?" queried Sergeant Lindsay.

"I've never worked since my wife died and some time ago I promised my daughter that she could go on an expensive school holiday abroad," Reid whispered, "and it was obvious that I couldn't afford the expense of it all so rather than disappoint my wee lassie I stupidly thought up this daft idea of forging Miss Cook's will and getting my hands on some money," he continued in a voice that was full of remorse. "But tell me, sergeant," queried Reid, "I think I made a good job of copying Miss Cook's handwriting so how, without checking, did you know so quickly that my attempt at the will was a forgery?"

"Mr. Reid, you're gonna kick yourself when I tell you," replied the sergeant, "but in the genuine will made out by Miss Cook she left all her money to you! She would hardly make out another with the same instructions!"

Reid's behaviour also meant that the genuine will in his favour was no longer valid!

THE COBBLER'S MARK

The curious thing about solving a crime is that the breakthrough in the case can often stem from something coming to light during enquiries into a completely different offence, totally unconnected to the first one.

This was exactly what happened in the downfall of local thief and troublemaker, Dave Robb.

Robb had lived all his 25 years in the town and was well-known to practically everyone, police and public alike.

It all started on a Friday evening during the summer holiday period when Cecil Milne, manager of the cinema in the High Street, phoned the local police station. "You'd better get down here straight away," reported Cecil in an excited voice, "there's a boy here in the cinema queue causing an awfy rammy."

Police Sergeant McPherson and new recruit, Police Constable Gordon, went to the High Street where, outside the picture house, a large queue had gathered while waiting on the matinee finishing. Sure enough, there was Dave Robb under the influence of alcohol making a pest of himself by shouting, bawling and generally committing a breach of the peace.

When warned about his conduct, Robb became even more aggressive and started to struggle with the officers.

"Cuff him, cuff him," Sergeant McPherson shouted to the inexperienced constable who quickly responded by giving the rowdy Mr. Robb a tremendous wallop round the ear.

"For goodness sake, I meant put the handcuffs on him," yelled Sergeant McPherson with a worried look of disbelief on his face!

However, the clip round the ear seemed to work wonders because Robb calmed down. He was taken to the police station and put in a cell until he sobered up and probably because Robb made no complaint about his treatment, Sergeant McPherson told him he would simply be released, when sober, and let off with a warning as to his future conduct.

Poor probationary Constable Gordon also got a stern warning from his sergeant along with a more detailed briefing on police jargon.

While prisoners are detained in police cells, it is procedure to divest them of their belongings. Their footwear is left outside the cell door and it was here that Robb's predicament became much more serious. Property and footwear is automatically checked by CID officers to see if there is any link to unsolved crimes.

It was during this check that Detective Constable Souter examined Robb's shoes and discovered something of great interest. A repair pattern on the heel matched that of a footprint found at the scene of a more serious crime which had taken place some three months earlier.

Willie Barr, a retired railway clerk, had returned home one night and disturbed an intruder in his house. In the darkness a struggle ensued and the elderly Mr. Barr was savagely attacked before the hooligan made good his escape. However, the bruiser had left a very distinct footprint in the garden and an impression of this was photographed and later filed away with the report in the 'cases unsolved' category.

Amongst the small amount of property stolen was an 1897 Queen Victoria Crown piece. Searching out the relative file, Detective Constable Souter checked Robb's shoes with the photographic impression taken at the scene of the beastly attack. Souter was thrilled to discover that these shoes were, without doubt, the footwear which had made the impression.

Constable Souter questioned Robb when he sobered up (Robb that is!). The villain strongly denied being responsible and although he agreed that the shoes found in his possession had obviously made the footprint his explanation quickly disheartened Constable Souter. The suspect was adamant that he had bought the shoes four weeks earlier at a Scout jumble sale in the town hall and he further alleged that the person who donated the shoes must have been the culprit as the crime had taken place 12 weeks earlier.

Robb was warned about his breach of the peace charge and released in his stocking soles due to his shoes being retained pending more enquiries.

Souter now had the arduous task of checking all those people who helped out at the jumble sale and he learned that among the junk items such as shoes were sold but no one could recall selling any to Robb.

Jean Brown, one of the helpers, did remember something quite out of the ordinary though and this revived Constable Souter's enthusiasm. Miss Brown knew Robb. He had been at the sale and was interested in a wireless which was on the stall. He told Miss

Brown that he had no money but would she accept a crown coin for the radio. After all, she could sell the coin quite easily as it was 'a collector's piece', Robb reminded Miss Brown.

She agreed and accepted the coin which was sold at the jumble sale the same day. Miss Brown could not recall who had bought the coin and all she could say was that it was a Victorian crown. Souter later discussed his progress with Detective Inspector Murdoch. "If he's denying it, Souter, you'll have difficulty trying tae prove it." said the Inspector. "We know Robb had a Victorian crown and we know his shoes left the tell-tale footprint but we cannae prove he had the shoes at the time Barr was attacked."

Inspector Murdoch stared at the shoes and after a long silence he said, "I've got an idea, Souter. This heel repair on the shoes is of such an individual style that maybe, just maybe, one of the cobblers in the town will recognise it as his work."

Souter called on Jimmy Logan, the most popular of the shoe repairers and immediately the amiable cobbler recognised the repair work as coming from his own hand.

"This is crucial, Jimmy," said Souter, "but could you possibly tell me when you did this repair and the name of the customer?"

"I can tell you exactly," said the obliging cobbler, "because I have my own method of tagging the customers' shoes when they first come in for repair. Inside the tongue of each shoe I write the date and the customer's name in ink so it will not fade," continued Jimmy as he undid the laces of one of the shoes. Souter gasped with delight as Jimmy pulled back the tongue to reveal 'D. Robb, January 2' written in ink.

Souter returned to the police station with the latest twist in the tale.

"This proves that Robb had thae shoes long before the crime took place and he could not have possibly bought them at the Scout jumble sale," Souter said to his inspector.

"Good work, Souter," said Murdoch. "I have tae admit I would never have thought aboot looking below the tongue of a shoe tae solve a crime."

Robb, when confronted with the new evidence, admitted the crime and was taken back into custody. While he was being arrested he quickly put his arms up over his head and covered his ears. "Strange chap," muttered Murdoch, not knowing the real reason for Robb's behaviour.

A SIZZLING EXPERIENCE

Graham Young was a paltry little thief who never lost an opportunity to pursue his lawbreaking lifestyle.

One forenoon while visiting the Eastgate shops he noticed something which stimulated his cunning criminal mind. The shops in question lay in a fairly isolated area, some distance away from dwelling houses.

Public access was at the front while the secluded rear of the premises was used mainly by delivery vehicles. What really aroused Young's interest was the presence of a vacant shop sandwiched between the jewellers and the butchers.

The jeweller's shop lay to the right of the vacant premises with the butchers on the left. The villain quickly realised how easy it would be to break into the jewellers from the inside of the empty premises and a notice on the door convinced him that it would be even simpler getting into this shop.

The notice intimated that any interested parties seeking to let the shop could pick up the keys at the local estate agents nearby. Young did just that but instead of using the keys to view the shop he took the rear door key to the ironmongers and had a duplicate cut.

Returning the keys to the estate agent, Young made the excuse that the vacant shop was unsuitable for his purpose and his actions did not arouse any suspicion. Young could now enter the empty shop using the rear door key then lock the door behind him.

During the night under the cover of darkness his plan was to chip away at the adjoining wall to get into the jeweller's shop. In all his previous escapades Young had been a dismal failure. He was the dead duck, the non-starter, who always seemed to end up in the police cells but this time the hopeful rogue was sure nothing could go amiss.

Young decided that as soon as darkness fell on Friday night he would go ahead with his plan. Armed with a holdall containing torch, hammer and chisel, the villain stealthily made his way to the rear of the shops. He was in a highly excited state as he fumbled in the pitch dark to open the rear door of the empty shop with his duplicate key.

Once inside he locked the door behind him then set to work

with the hammer and chisel. It seemed to take hours as he chipped away at the mutual brick wall but eventually he succeeded in getting a hole large enough to squeeze through into the adjoining premises.

Young's intention was to fill his holdall with as many small items of jewellery as he could lay his hands on. The possibilities were mind boggling as he pushed the holdall first through the hole. He then squeezed and wriggled his way through, tearing his jacket in the process.

Once inside the occupied premises he stood up, brushed the dust off himself and briefly switched on his torch. He was in the butchers!

"How the heck can this be?" he said out loud.

It suddenly dawned on him. From the front the jewellers was to the right of the empty shop but he had entered from the rear so he should have set about the left wall. Due to his jumpy, keyed-up state, he had made the most monumental blunder of all and as it was nearing daytime he could not go back and start all over again on the opposite wall.

Rather than the night being a total failure, Young decided to fill his holdall with sausages and beef otherwise he would have to go home empty handed. Later in the day, the burglary was discovered when Henry Bell, the butcher, opened his shop for the day's business.

Detective Inspector Archie Murdoch and Detective Constable Souter were quickly on the scene and their enquiries included a visit to the estate agents. The officers were quick to realise what had happened.

"There's only wan man in the toon capable of botching up a job like this," said the Inspector.

"Aye, Graham Young," came the reply from Constable Souter.

"We'll pay him a visit later on, Souter," said Archie, "because I want to check the file first on the Barton's job."

The inspector was referring to a major theft of jewellery from Bartons the jewellers some time back and the entry to the premises bore similarities to the present one.

"Mind you," said the inspector, "Ah dinnae think for a minute that Graham Young is capable of the Barton job. It wis a bit too professional for the likes of him."

Later in the afternoon the officers decided to call on Young and as they walked up the garden path they could smell the frying steak a mile away!

Inspector Murdoch was normally a serious-minded officer but as he and Souter knocked on the suspect's door he couldn't stop laughing.

Young answered the door. Calming himself down, Inspector Murdoch informed the villain of the nature of the enquiry. Inside the house, Mrs. Young and the four bairns were all getting tucked into juicy steaks for their tea.

"Is that good, son?" Archie said to one of the youngsters.

"Aye, and we had steak fir oor breakfast as well," replied the wee boy innocently.

By this time Young knew the game was up. Young was one of life's losers and he always adopted the 'fair cop' attitude and he held his wrist in front of him, saying, "Stick on the handcuffs Archie."

The inspector started to tell Young that he would be arrested for breaking into a butcher's shop when he again got an uncontrollable fit of the giggles.

"Wis it theft of diamonds from a butchers, Souter, or theft o' sausages from the jewellers?" blurted the Inspector. Still chortling away, Archie closed his notebook and put it in his pocket.

"We'll sort oot the charges later on," he said. Young, who stood to lose the most, saw the funny side but then he became quite serious.

"Inspector, what would you say if we worked oot a deal? I can tell you who done the Barton's job if you turn a blind eye to twa or three pound of sausages."

Inspector Murdoch was definitely interested as the break-in at Bartons involved items of great value. "If what you tell me, Graham, leads to the arrest of the villains and recovery of the property I'm sure I could get Henry Bell, the butcher, to come roond tae my way of thinking," said the inspector.

Young supplied information which brought about a successful conclusion to both cases. Graham Young had experience in the building trade and as part of the deal he made good the damage to the wall of the vacant shop.

"You gave me a chance, Archie," said Graham to the inspector, "and you'll see I'll no' let you down."

At the end of his tour of duty, Inspector Murdoch was glad to get home and and put his feet up following a good day's work.

"Whit's for tea?" he asked.

"Sausages," said Mrs. Murdoch!

MOORE'S ALMANAC

Peter Duncan was a retired elderly gentleman who lived alone since the passing of his wife Martha some years previously.

One Sunday evening following a weekend visit to his brother's home Duncan returned to find that someone had broken into his home and stolen numerous items. What disturbed him most was the theft of a small carriage clock which had been given to him many years ago by his former workmates on the occasion of his marriage. The timepiece had great sentimental value and was inscribed on the reverse 'To Peter and Martha, June 1935.'

In the weeks that followed, several other dwelling houses in the district were broken into and in each case the culprit had gained entry by forcing sash windows with a long curved blade similar to the type of knife used by carpet fitters. The spate of burglaries reached new heights, however, when the Fire Brigade were summoned to a blaze at the home of Miss Allan, an elderly lady who lived alone. The inferno had been confined to a bedroom but the drama unfolded when the firemen discovered the charred body of Miss Allan among the debris.

"It looks like she got out of bed and knocked over this paraffin heater," said the leading fireman to Detective Inspector Murdoch who took charge at the scene. After a close, harrowing inspection of the mortal remains, Murdoch said: "I don't think so. Miss Allan was, in my opinion, dead before the fire started."

"What mak's ye think that?" queried the fireman.

"Well, had she been alive at the time of the fire there would be damage and blisters to the skin tissue," said the Inspector.

As common in fires of this nature, there was a terrible stench in the house and this prompted the Inspector to go outside and see if Constable Souter was making any progress examining the locus.

"This is gonna disturb you, sir," said Souter, "but Miss Allan has had a visit from our burglar."

"If we solve the earlier break-ins, we'll automatically solve this one," said Murdoch.

The first breakthrough came when the officers found the knife which had been used to force open the window. It had obviously been dropped while the culprit in his panic made good his escape.

The knife was branded New Carpet Co. on the wooden handle and both officers knew that a firm using this name traded from a small unit on the industrial estate. Lengthy enquiries there confirmed that the knife belonged to the company but the disappointing outcome was that all the carpet fitters past and present were eventually eliminated from the enquiry. In the interval a post-mortem examination revealed that Miss Allan had simply died of a heart attack. There were no indications of assault and it was confirmed by the pathologist that she was in fact dead prior to the fire as predicted earlier by Murdoch.

"Where do we go from here?" the Inspector asked Souter. "We have a string of break-ins, a death, a carpet fitter's knife but nae suspects."

Weeks passed and no progress was made but, strangely enough, no further break-ins had taken place. Peter Duncan, the first victim of these burglaries, spent some of his time browsing at the local auction room owned by Sandy Hay and it was there that this enquiry gained momentum. Among the lots offered for the forthcoming sale was Peter Duncan's carriage clock. It still bore the inscription and was without doubt the same timepiece that had previously been stolen from Duncan's home. Sandy Hay, who was most helpful on these matters, told Inspector Murdoch that old Miss Jarvis had put the clock in for sale. Miss Jarvis was a frail, elderly lady and hardly the type of person who would be going about breaking into other people's houses. Nevertheless, she would have to be questioned and the officers paid her a visit.

Miss Jarvis was taken aback when told of the nature of the enquiry and she informed the officers that she had bought the clock from Moore's second hand shop in the arcade. This was some time ago and because the timepiece was not working properly she decided to get rid of it at the auction.

Inspector Murdoch and Souter called at the arcade, only to discover that the premises were boarded up and Moore had ceased trading. They then continued their enquiries at Moore's home where they learned that, since closing down, Moore had chucked out all his records and books which meant he was unable to say who had sold him the clock. He did admit selling the timepiece to Miss Jarvis.

"Have you ever had a job as a carpet fitter?" the suspicious Inspector asked.

"Never," came the nervous reply from Moore who by this time appeared to be getting quite agitated.

"I'm afraid you'll have to come down to the police station while enquiries are being continued," the Inspector told Moore.

A warrant to search the suspect's home was obtained and the only item of interest found was a pair of dungarees.

"Smell these," said Murdoch, holding the garment below Constable Souter's nose.

"Phew, they're stinking o' paraffin," Souter gasped.

"Aye," said Archie, with a disgruntled sigh, "but it's no' enough tae prove he's oor man."

The officers returned to the police station and further questioning of the suspect turned out to be a waste of time.

"We'll just have to let him go," muttered the Inspector, "but stick him back in a cell the noo while we pay another visit tae the New Carpet Company."

The officers called there and again were disappointed to learn that Moore had never been employed there. It was then that Constable Souter came up with a most interesting thought. "Has Moore ever been a customer of the New Carpet Company?" he queried.

The firm's order books were checked and, remarkably enough, it was discovered that about 10 months previously Moore had a carpet fitted in the living room of his home. The carpet fitter who had done the work was interviewed and his account was startling. He recalled fitting the carpet at Moore's home and some remnants were left over which Moore said he could use for carpeting a small cupboard. "He didna have a knife tae cut the bits of carpet so I left him mine," said the carpet fitter. Inspector Murdoch produced the knife found at Miss Allan's house and the carpet fitter confirmed that this was the one he had given Moore.

This was the development the Inspector was awaiting and he and Souter dashed back to the police station to confront the suspect with the latest findings.

"Has Moore said anything since we left?" queried the Inspector.

"No, he's just sat in the cell reading his almanac," quipped Sergeant Lindsay who liked a joke.

Inspector Murdoch was not amused.

When all the evidence was laid before him, Moore finally broke down and confessed to all the break-ins including the tragic case at Miss Allan's.

His version of events was later confirmed by forensic and medical experts. Moore had broken into Miss Allan's house and, by a remarkable coincidence, he found her dead on the bedroom floor. She had died of natural causes but Moore panicked, feared a possible homicide charge and so he spilled the paraffin heater and deliberately set fire to the house in a bungled attempt to make Miss Allan's death appear a horrible accident.

"Pop him back in a cell," Murdoch instructed Sergeant Lindsay.

"Give him his almanac tae read until we get him tae court in the morning," spluttered Murdoch who by this time was in a much happier frame of mind.

ASSAULT AND ROBBERY

One of the most bewildering, mysterious set of circumstances and events turned out to have the simplest of explanations but it took months before the solution to it all unfolded.

On the morning of June 6th John Graham appeared at the Sheriff Court where he had earlier tendered a plea of 'not guilty' to driving a car without having a driving licence.

His trial began immediately and lasted until lunchtime when the Sheriff on hearing all the evidence found Graham guilty.

Graham was a neat, smartly dressed character and he wore a red jerkin and grey trousers at the time of his court appearance. During the same forenoon, elderly Mrs. Reid was shopping in the High Street when she was subjected to a frightening attack which left her in a shocked and confused state.

A youth, wearing a red jerkin and grey trousers, had sneaked up behind her then suddenly knocked her to the ground and made off with her handbag containing a fair amount of money. The youth ran off down the street which was thronged with other shoppers who were unaware of the attack on Mrs. Reid.

In response to a frantic telephone call from a shopkeeper nearby, Detective Sergeant Lindsay promptly made his way to the scene where witnesses quickly gave a description of the suspect. Another witness thought he had seen the assailant get into a small blue sports car which was parked further down the road.

Mrs. Reid in the meantime was taken to hospital suffering from bruising and shock. She was later able to tell the police that the handbag stolen from her was made from crocodile skin but her description of the attacker was somewhat vague.

On returning to the police station, Sergeant Lindsay and Constable Souter were travelling north on Factory Road when they encountered a blue sports car travelling in the opposite direction. The young driver was wearing a red jerkin! The car and driver matched quite accurately the description given earlier by witnesses. The officers pursued the sports car and soon it was brought to a halt.

The driver gave his name as John Graham and apart from the red jerkin he was also seen to be wearing grey trousers. Sergeant Lindsay was sure he had Mrs. Reid's attacker and he was taken to the police station.

Graham was searched and his personal property was put in a big buff coloured envelope while he was detained, pending enquiries.

Detective Inspector Archie Murdoch was now placed in charge of the enquiry. "Where were you at 11 o'clock this morning?" he asked the suspect Graham. The reply from the accused left the entire police investigation team surprised and dejected.

"I was in the Sheriff Court all morning," Graham replied, "and there's a Sheriff, a Procurator Fiscal and umpteen policemen who were also there and they can vouch for me," he concluded in a cocky, arrogant manner.

Inspector Murdoch summoned two of the officers who had been in court to the interview room where Graham was being questioned.

Looking at the suspect, one of the officers, Constable Davidson, said, "There's nae doubt aboot it, that's the same John Graham that was in court this morning."

"He couldnae have assaulted Mrs. Reid in the High Street this forenoon," commented the other officer.

Hearing the testimony of the two court officers, Inspector Murdoch had no option but to release John Graham. The suspect was given back his belongings which comprised an amount of money, driving licence and a bunch of keys.

Graham's signature was necessary on the property register to acknowledge receipt of his effects and as he wrote with the pen in his left hand Inspector Murdoch saw a gold sovereign ring on the suspect's little finger.

John Graham was released and eliminated from the enquiry, leaving the officers with little or nothing to go on. Fortunately, Mrs. Reid recovered from her ordeal and suffered no lasting effects despite her alarming experience.

Months of fruitless enquiries were made and the case eventually remained unsolved so the file was condemned to gather dust on the shelf unless something fresh cropped up which would justify reopening the investigation.

Almost a year later Inspector Murdoch was in the police canteen having tea with several other officers. It was customary on these occasions to talk over particular crimes which had gone unsolved and inevitably the robbery case involving John Graham was brought up.

Suddenly the quiet conversation was interrupted.

"That's it, that's it!" exclaimed Inspector Murdoch, banging his fist with such force on the table that he dislocated his little finger. In excruciating pain, Murdoch didn't continue with what had aroused him but fortunately Constable Watson who was highly trained in first aid was able to re-align the Inspector's little pinky.

"Jings, thanks Watson, that wis sair," said Murdoch, looking a bit sheepish and clasping his sore hand with the other.

"Are ye going tae tell what it is about the John Graham case that has created a' this excitement, Archie?" said Sergeant Lindsay, smiling.

"Oh aye, now where was I?" queried Murdoch, regaining his composure.

"It's just dawned on me after all these months," said Archie, lighting his pipe, "but how is it that John Graham had a driving licence among his belongings when two hoors earlier he was found guilty at the Sheriff Court of driving without a licence?"

Sergeant Lindsay dashed off to the unsolved files and sure enough the records showed this to be the case! "How did we not spot this at the time?" said the bewildered Sergeant, scratching his head in disbelief.

"It's a classic case of no seeing the wood fir the trees," replied the Inspector, "now let's get doon tae Graham's hoose and see what he has tae say for himself."

Murdoch was prone to keeping his little suspicions to himself but everyone knew from his mannerisms that the Inspector was now following a very definite line of enquiry. The wry smile etched on his face usually implied that a successful result was not far away.

The suspect John Graham lived in a neighbouring town in the county and as a result the officers knew little or nothing about him. On the way to their quarry Inspector Murdoch stopped at the Town House where he had a word with the registrar and a look at his records.

"Wis it his collection o' Jimmy Shand records ye were looking at Archie?" joked Sergeant Lindsay.

"Dinnae be cheeky now, Lindsay," retorted the Inspector who was also in high spirits with the knowledge that the crime was about to be solved.

Calling at the suspect John Graham's house, the officers were invited inside. Graham, when informed of the reason for the visit, again denied having been involved in the attack on Mrs. Reid.

"I want you to sign your name here," said the Inspector,

handing the suspect a piece of paper and a pencil. Using his right hand, the now nervous John Graham signed his name, much to the Inspector's delight.

"The last time you signed your name for us, Mr. Graham, you used your left hand," remarked Murdoch, "or correct me if I'm wrang but it wouldn't happen to be yer identical twin brother, Peter, that we had locked up after the robbery!" Murdoch had checked the registrars and found that identical twins were born to Mr. and Mrs. Graham 20 years ago. The brothers had used this deception, of identity and alibi, to their advantage on more than one criminal venture and both were charged that "while acting together" they robbed Mrs. Reid.

Later that night at the pub the officers were celebrating their success. "Archie, you must have a double," said Sergeant Lindsay, handing him a large Scotch.

THE BUTTON

During the July 'fair fortnight' it was very quiet in the town and it seemed as if everyone was away on their annual holiday.

Enjoying the quiet spell, Detective Inspector Archie Murdoch sat at his desk, doodling over a crossword but unknown to him at this time a terrible crime was being discovered some 300 miles away. A sickening crime which, through a twist of fate , was to involve Inspector Murdoch himself, despite the fact that it was well outside his police area.

What made this wicked offence even more ominous was the fact that the person discovering the atrocity was a local man, bachelor Andrew Smillie. Smillie was making his way home from a holiday in England when he stopped his car in a lay-by to exercise his dog in an adjoining woodland. On doing so, Smillie made the dreadful discovery of a young girl's body amongst the ferns and shrubs. The child had apparently been strangled and Smillie alerted another motorist to summon the police.

A major police enquiry swung into action and it was soon learned that the child had been abducted from a nearby town earlier that day.

Smillie's version of events was plausible and the English police officers had no reason to suspect him at this time and he was allowed to continue his journey home.

The following day, as is procedure in these cases, Detective Inspector Murdoch received a request from his English colleagues to note a more detailed statement from his witness. Perhaps, having had time to think, Smillie could supply more information. The Inspector duly called on Smillie and he more or less repeated how he had discovered the body of the unfortunate child.

Again, there was no reason to suspect Smillie at this juncture. His car was thoroughly checked and nothing untoward was found.

About a month later the Inspector was in his office when Constable Fraser came in. "Just had a report, sir, of a man attempting to abduct a bairn," he said. Such a serious and disturbing report immediately raised Murdoch's eyebrows. A local child, eight-year-old Alison Ferrie, had been in the town's main street when a man in a blue car stopped to ask directions to the Crown Hotel. The motorist opened his passenger door to speak to Alison then suddenly pulled her into the car. Fortunately the child screamed and struggled free from the vehicle. She had arrived home in a very distressed state and her mother immediately reported the incident to the police.

Inspector Murdoch spoke to the child who had surprisingly calmed down but she was unable to give a clear description of the car or the man who had attempted to abduct her.

At the time, Alison had worn a wine coloured coat and when examined a number of dog hairs were found sticking to it. A dark red button was also missing from the garment but neither Alison nor her mum could say when this button was lost. It could have fallen off weeks ago.

This disturbing case would be most difficult to prove. There were no witnesses and if the culprit was traced it would simply be his word against that of an eight-year-old child.

Despite relentless enquiries the case remained unsolved and some officers even voiced the opinion that Alison may have invented or dreamed up the abduction story.

Enquiries became exhausted and reports on the case were filed away. Alison's coat was put in the station production cupboard for future examination if necessary.

In the weeks that followed, Inspector Murdoch had a new headache in so far that he was becoming inundated with reports of cars being broken into and property stolen. These thefts were happening nearly every night and what made matters worse was the report that Superintendent Duncan's wife had fallen victim of the car thief.

"The Super's breathing doon ma neck, Souter," pleaded Archie. "I want every car that's broken intae given a really thorough check for prints. We've got tae catch the thief otherwise we'll both be back ploddin' the beat if Duncan gets any mair annoyed."

The Inspector's outburst was interrupted by the phone ringing. It was Andrew Smillie reporting that his car had been broken into whilst parked overnight outside the Crown Hotel. Reporting that he was the victim of a crime was Smillie's fateful and costly mistake but, at this point, no one suspected anything out of the ordinary.

"Go and check Smillie's car thoroughly for fingerprints and dinnae leave a stane unturned," Murdoch instructed Souter.

Constable Souter soon returned with his findings which at first disappointed Murdoch.

"There wis nae fingerprints, sir, no' even a button," said Souter who then quickly corrected himself. "Well, in fact that's not quite the case because it turned out a button was the only thing I found in the car. It was down the seat and could have come from the thief's jacket," concluded Souter as he showed his Inspector a dark red button.

The look on the Inspector's face was priceless as he excitedly bellowed, "The Crown Hotel!" then dashed off to the filing cupboard and pulled out the old police reports.

"Here it is, Souter," gasped Archie, holding the report relating to the attempted abduction of Alison Ferrie. "The scoundrel asked Alison fir directions tae the Crown Hotel!" Rushing to the production cupboard the Inspector got out Alison's coat and surprise, surprise, the button found in Smillie's car was the one missing from the child's garment. "Do ye ken whit this means?" blurted the tumultuous Inspector. "If Smillie tried to abduct wee Alison then he also abducted and killed that bairn in England."

While Smillie was being apprehended, the officers noted the presence of his labrador dog in the house. Samples of dogs' hair were later expertly tested and found to match precisely those traces found on Alison's coat. Smillie was harshly questioned and eventually admitted the attempted abduction of Alison Ferrie but he at first vehemently denied the horrible, unforgivable offence in England. Inspector Murdoch had by this time obtained a photograph of the lovely, innocent child taken at school before she met her revolting, beastly end. Saying nothing, the Inspector held the sinless child's photo just one foot away from Smillie's face and demanded that he look at it. Smillie stared coldly at the photo and just as the Inspector's patience was wearing out, the conscience-stricken beast burst into tears. Sobbing uncontrollably, Smillie admitted the vile offence. He was later escorted to England where, following a court appearance, he was committed to a mental institution. Back home, the spate of car thefts continued but somehow Superintendent Duncan had given up pressurising Murdoch for a result on Mrs. Duncan's car. Apparently she smashed it into a lamp-post a few days later and she and the 'super' were not on talking terms.

"According tae the wife," quipped Superintendent Duncan, "the lamp-post jumped oot in front of her!"

THE SLATES

Miss Chalmers was an elderly spinster who lived alone in her two-storey house in the town's Church Street.

The house was an old Victorian property and not surprisingly the odd slate had blown off the roof with recent high winds.

It was just a normal autumn afternoon when she answered the front door. Standing on the doorstep were two men who handed her a card which also listed a city telephone number and address.

Builder Kevin Michael David Banks had already seen the name of the householder on the doorplate and he calmly introduced himself. "Hello, Miss Chalmers, it's very fortunate that you're at home because I've just finished repairing some slates on Mr. Simpson the lawyer's house and very luckily for you I have some material left from this job."

Unknown to Miss Chalmers, she was about to become the unfortunate victim of the 'bogus workman'. These callous, detestable villains prey on the elderly. "Whit dae ye mean, ma lucky day," replied a bewildered Miss Chalmers.

"Well," said Banks, "while passing by I noticed slates missing on your roof and we can quickly remedy this for you, especially now when I just happen to have with me those spare slates from Mr. Simpson's job."

Banks quickly added, "I feel, as a professional builder, it is only fair that I should tell you that unless you have the work done now, the rain will get into your house and cause dry rot and this is very expensive and very messy."

"A stitch in time, Miss Chalmers," interrupted the other man, James Edward Kenny.

Looking up to the roof where Banks was pointing, Miss Chalmers consented to the missing slates being replaced. She was so anxious at the possible consequences of rain damage that she practically held the ladder for the men who went on to the roof and out of her view.

About an hour later Banks and Kenny came down and announced that the slates were now intact.

"That will be £10," he demanded. Ten pounds then was the equivalent of one week's wages but rather than protest at the

30

excessive cost Miss Chalmers handed over two £5 notes. After this money was safely in Banks' pocket he stunned Miss Chalmers by saying, "You've a major problem up on the roof which cannae be seen from down here. The chimney is ready to fall down and if it injures someone you can be sued for a lot of money."

"Not only that, Miss Chalmers," butted-in Kenny, "if that chimney fell on to your roof it would cause major damage."

These alarming comments brought Miss Chalmers close to tears and she became quite distressed. "Calm down, miss," said the villain Banks in a reassuring voice. "Get £50 in cash and we'll come back tomorrow and put things safe and for no extra cost I'll also fix your gutters which are in a bad state."

The following day, as agreed, the polite talking conmen returned and went on the roof. Eventually they came down and assured the unsuspecting Miss Chalmers that all was now in order and she handed over the £50 which was, in fact, all her cash savings. While all this was taking place, a neighbour phoned the police to express her concern about the men opposite.

Sergeant Lindsay, who received the call, was quick to suspect 'bogus workmen' were working in the area. He and D.C. Souter dashed to the scene just in time because Banks and Kenny were loading ladders on to their van and about to make a hasty retreat.

Miss Chalmers was unaware that she had been the victim of deception and was reluctant to make an official complaint at this time.

The two scoundrels were detained at the police station and they had been in this situation before. Banks was arrogant and confident he could talk his way out. After all, it was their word against that of Miss Chalmers.

"We done some repair work tae the auld wife's chimney and gutters and charged her a fiver fir our trouble," he said despite £50 in £5 notes being found in his possession. Kenny gave the same account and it was obvious that their explanation had been rehearsed. They strenuously denied receiving £50 for the work.

Detective Inspector Archie Murdoch was briefed on the circumstances. "Young Constable Fraser was a builder before he joined the force," said Murdoch. "We'll get him up on that roof to see what work if any has been done."

The Inspector and Constable Fraser returned to the scene and on examining the roof Fraser reported: "The chimney's never been touched and similarly there's no been any work carried out on the roof," he said. "I'm afraid Miss Chalmers has paid for works which have never been done."

Miss Chalmers now realised she had been falsely induced to part with all her cash savings. "Some of these £5 notes I had set aside for my electricity, insurance, rates and other accounts," she said. "In fact, I wrote on the bank notes what each was for. The fiver I set aside for insurance I wrote 'insurance' on it and so on."

"Miss Chalmers," said an astonished Inspector, "it's against the law tae write on bank notes but we'll overlook that because this is the best possible thing you could have told me."

The officers obtained samples of her handwriting and returned to the office to confront the vile pair of villains. Sure enough, on the bank notes taken from the accused were written the words 'rates', 'electricity', 'insurance' and so on and this matched perfectly with the specimens of handwriting by the victim.

Confirmation of the handwriting analysis was later secured from the experts at the Identification Bureau in the city who assisted the other constabularies in these matters.

The 'bogus workmen' on this occasion were out of luck and they were sent to prison. Miss Chalmers, unlike other elderly people who fell foul of these criminals, was fortunate to have her money recovered.

On returning the money, Inspector Murdoch said, "Miss Chalmers, let me tell you, and you should tell all your friends that you should never, never allow people who call uninvited to do work of this kind. You must always get in touch with the local builders and get one or two estimates. The local builders are only too happy to give you a free estimate and you should never hand over cash or any payment until you're sure the work has been carried out in a satisfactory manner."

"I'm sorry, Mr. Murdoch," she said, "I'll be a lot mair careful in the future."

"If you've any doubts just phone the police station immediately. We're only too happy to help."

"Oh, Mr. Murdoch," said Miss Chalmers, running after him, "will I get fined for writing on thae bank notes?"

"Dinna be daft, Miss Chalmers," said Archie with a smile. "I'm awfy glad you did because that's how we were able to prove that the £50 was the amount given by you to the two rogues and not merely £5 as they claimed."

TWO MINDS AT WORK

It was the long autumn weekend, and Detective Inspector Archie Murdoch had managed to get away from all worries at the police station.

He and his missus had returned to Mrs MacFadyean's caravan site at Ullapool for a long weekend holiday, having been there some months earlier for a summer vacation.

On the summer holiday, the inspector had made a dubious purchase of a duty-free camera and some vodka from Dimitri, one of the Russian fishermen, who berthed regularly in Loch Broom. Murdoch had left these black market goods behind during his summer stay, and Mrs MacFadyean had found them in the caravan occupied by the Murdochs after they left.

"Its awfy nice tae see you again," greeted Mrs MacFadyean, "and here's yer camera and vodka, just as ye left it," she continued, as she handed over the goods to a grateful and relieved Inspector Murdoch.

Murdoch was relieved because he initially thought the bootlegged goods had been stolen,and the prospect of the matter coming to the attention of the local constabulary may have been embarrassing to say the least. Mrs MacFadyean left the couple to settle in their caravan, and it wasn't long before Murdoch was in a happy, relaxed holiday mood.

The calm, serene beauty of Ullapool, on the shores of Loch Broom, with the Summer Isles beyond, was sheer bliss. Murdoch sat peering out of his caravan window admiring the view while Mrs Murdoch made a cup of tea. Suddenly the calm peace was broken as Murdoch let out a gasp. "Oh my Goad, take a look oot the windae,"he exclaimed.

Mrs Murdoch looked curiously out the window, straining her neck to see what was amiss.

"I cannae see onythin' Archie,jist mair caravans and tents.What are ye goin' oan aboot?" she queried.

"Look at the face boggling oot the caravan windae opposite, do ye ken wha' it is?" asked Murdoch. "No," Mrs Murdoch quietly responded.

"Its Dougie Mitchell fae doon oor way. He's the biggest small time crook on ma patch," said Archie as he referred to Mitchell, who was a pest, a small-time opportunist thief, who could not resist the temptation to steal. He had frequently been a bee in Murdoch's bonnet over the years.

"This is a' ah need for a happy holiday weekend,"grunted Archie as he scratched the back of his head in disbelief. "Och jist forget aboot him and relax Archie," said the missus in a comforting tone as she poured him a large glass of vodka.

The rest of that day and night Archie sulked a bit,and stayed in his caravan. It had rained anyway, and this made the task of staying indoors a bit easier. Normally on these caravan holidays Archie is wakened in the morning by the sound of sausages sizzling in the frying pan as Mrs Murdoch prepares the breakfast, but the following day he was aroused by a loud knocking and banging at the caravan door.

Awakened from his sleep a bleary-eyed Murdoch opened the caravan door and there stood Police Sergeant Robbie MacPhee of the Ullapool Constabulary.

"I'm awfy sorry tae disturb ye,"said the sergeant,"But ye widnae happen tae have heard or seen anything suspicious during the nicht?"

"No," said Murdoch, "Ah sleep like a log when I'm here. It must be the sea air." The sergeant went on to say that during the night, a number of unlocked cars at the site had been entered, and a variety of goods stolen.

"Some of the tourists have lost cameras, binoculars and clothing from their vehicles," said the Sergeant. Murdoch introduced himself as a fellow police officer, and invited Sergeant MacPhee into the caravan.

"You should find oot what him opposite wis gettin' up tae, Sergeant," said Murdoch, pointing to the caravan occupied by the villain Mitchell.

"Just call me Robbie," said the sergeant as he peered out of the window. "But there's no anybody in that caravan Archie, it looks empty!" Sure enough,when both the officers went to check, Dougie Mitchell had disappeared. He had obviously scarpered during the night.

Murdoch strongly suspected Mitchell of being responsible for the spate of thefts. "After all he didnae notice that I was opposite him," said Archie, as he gave Sergeant MacPhee a description of the suspect and the vehicle he was in possession of.

At least Murdoch was relieved that Mitchell was no longer at the caravan site, and he could now relax and enjoy his weekend break.

Later that night Inspector Murdoch was in the Shore Bar, enjoying a beer, when Sergeant MacPhee came in, wearing civilian clothes. "Just the man I'm lookin' fur, let me buy you a drink," said the happy, smiling sergeant who was now off duty.

"Whit are ye celebratin' Robbie?" queried Murdoch.

"We arrested Dougie Mitchell this afternoon along at the Gairloch, and in his vehicle, we recovered all the goods stolen frae the tourists' cars,"exclaimed the sergeant who was cock-a-hoop at having such a quick conclusion to the crimes.

The two off-duty police officers certainly made the most of their celebration drink, as they methodically demolished one drink after another. The officers talked shop most of the time and exchanged accounts on a number of police matters.

"It's no exactly a crime, Archie, but thae foreign fishermen flogging their illicit, untaxed merchandise tae the tourists is a bit o' a headache fir me," said Sergeant MacPhee.

Archie decided not to mention his earlier purchases from Dimitri. Least said the better he thought to himself. Just at that who should come into the bar but Dimitri, and recognising Archie, he came straight over.

"Hello again Mr Murdieee,"said the foreign seaman, not quite remembering Archie's proper name. "And how are you getting on with that nice camera I sold you?" Poor Murdoch didn't know where to look and decided the best thing to do was order up another round of drinks. As the night progressed Archie noticed that Sergeant MacPhee's alcohol intake was increasing rapidly.

"Is somethin' botherin' ye Robbie,"queried Murdoch."Aye," replied the Sergeant, "And if ah dinnae get tae the bottom of it soon, it'll drive me tae drink," he sighed as he downed yet another whisky.

"Ah see yer having a wee rehearsal the nicht," commented Archie jokingly, as he enquired what the problem was. "There's a hotel here wi' a staff o' 20, and all summer there's been a spate of petty thefts from the visitors' rooms, and despite setting traps and everything else ah've never been able tae find oot who the culprit is,"explained the sergeant.

"But yer sure it's one o' the staff that's responsible for thae thefts?" queried Murdoch. "Aye, nae doobt aboot that," replied

Sergeant MacPhee. "There's nae doobt aboot that."

"Well," whispered Murdoch,"Ah'll tell whit tae dae the next time there's a theft at the hotel."

Sergeant MacPhee listened closely to Murdoch's suggestion. The following morning Sergeant MacPhee was back on duty, and as fate would have it, yet another theft had taken place at the hotel. In this instance a watch, belonging to a guest at the hotel, had been stolen, and the circumstances were such that the thief had to be a member of the staff.

Sergeant MacPhee went to the hotel and spoke to the proprietrix, Mrs Duncan. Deciding to put Murdoch's plan into action, the Sergeant asked Mrs Duncan for a private room, where he could interview each member of the staff individually. This was easily arranged and soon the sergeant was sitting at a table with the first member of staff sitting opposite.

"I have to tell you, as I'm telling all the rest of the staff, that this recent theft was a deliberate trap to catch the thief. The watch was dusted with fluorescent powder, and the culprit's hands will be stained. No matter how much washing is done, the stains will stay on the culprit's hands for days.

"Now these stains from the powder are not visible to the naked eye, but I will be returning tomorrow with a special fluorescent lamp, which will show up the powder marks, when the thief's hands are examined, so it would be better, if you are the culprit, to own up now, and avoid being embarrassed in front of your colleagues when I return tomorrow with the lamp for examination."

There was no response from the first staff member and Sergeant MacPhee repeated the same warning to each member individually. By the time had interviewed all of the staff he was down-hearted because his comments drew no response from anyone. Everyone had been firmly told that the stolen watch had been treated with powder, which would undoubtedly show up on the thief's hands, when inspected the following day with the lamp.

Later that night the sergeant was off duty and he met Inspector Murdoch in the lounge bar of Mrs Duncan's hotel.

The sergeant was about to reel off all the events concerning the interviews at the hotel when Mrs Duncan came over, smiling happily.

"The drinks are on me Sergeant MacPhee, and I'm awfy pleased tae tell ye that the matter of the thefts been resolved," She said. "Whit dae ye mean, Mrs Duncan, " asked a very bewildered Sergeant MacPhee.

"My chef, Wulllie Johnstone, disappeared just after ye left, and he has since phoned me from Inverness with his resignation. He's admitted stealing the watch and he said he couldnae bear the thoct of being humiliated in front of the others, when ye returned the morn' wi' yer lamp, and discovered the stains on his hands."

Mrs Duncan went on to say that Johnstone had admitted the other thefts at the hotel, and some of the property he had taken could be found in a kitchen cupboard.

"Aye," said Mrs Duncan gratefully to Sergeant MacPhee. "Yer lamp certainly did the trick." Handing the officers two large glasses of whisky, Mrs Duncan left to get on with other business.

After she left Sergeant MacPhee, with a great big smile on his face, turned to Murdoch and said,'Now whit lamp would that be I wonder." "Aye" joked Archie, "The lamp's like the pooder -- it disnae exist!"

The bluff had scared the culprit into panic, and following his telephone confession, he was later arrested for his felonies. On the Monday evening, Archie Murdoch was about to leave Ullapool after his amusing holiday weekend, when he was greeted by Sergeant MacPhee, who handed him a small bag.

"A present fir ye, Archie, with ma compliments,"said Sergeant MacPhee. Peering inside the bag, Archie found that it contained some very familiar looking bottles of vodka. "Ah see you've been talking tae an old freend o' mine," joked the inspector as he reminded the missus not to leave the goods behind this time!

THE SWINDLER

John Whitelaw spent most of his life defrauding people. His fine appearance, smart dress, and cultured well-mannered tone of voice was very re-assuring and these assets made his task of conning people so much easier.

He would pose as an ex-naval or army officer, a director, a doctor, or any profession that took his fancy. He had had total confidence in himself and made the task simple - bamboozling his victims was never a problem.

Whitelaw thought up a scheme to make easy money.One day he booked in at the Harbour Hotel, run by widow Mrs Hazel Mary Findlay.

"For how many nights?" queried the landlady as the formalities of signing the visitors' book were completed.

"Three nights perhaps five,"replied Whitelaw politely. Mrs Findlay showed her new guest his room, and he expressed his immediate delight as to how suitable and nice it was.

In the conversation that followed, Whitelaw stated that he was in the advertising and publishing business. "In fact," he disclosed,"I can be of great help to you and your hotel." The fraudster went into his briefcase and pulled out a magazine, which Mrs Findlay immediately recognised.

It was a copy of the popular monthly journal, 'Rural Scotland'. "I am senior advertising manager with the publishers, and at the moment, we're doing a special advertising feature on hotels, and as a special concession, I can offer you two free advertisements, if you book a minimum of three at the normal charge," he convincingly announced.

Mrs Findlay, who was a wee bit cautious, intimated that she would give the matter some thought... Later that night, in the hotel lounge bar,Findlay mingled with the other patrons, some resident and others just local customers in for a drink.

Findlay soon made a handful of friends with his smart talk, and it was not long before he was buying everyone a drink."Just put it on my bill, room number 17, "he told the barmaid. Whitelaw very quickly had everyone believing that he was a person of some wealth. He made a donation to the lifeboat fund collection box, which was on the bar counter, and he even bought a handful of lottery tickets which were also on sale at the bar.

The raffle was for a local charity and Whitelaw bought a number of tickets, because "it was for a grand cause and the first prize of a week's holiday on Arran would be just great for him, the wife and the kids."

Certainly everyone was impressed by the dapper John Whitelaw. Next morning at breakfast Mrs Findlay told the smooth talking guest that she would be interested in placing advertisements in 'Rural Scotland.' "You won't regret it Mrs Findlay," said the fraudster,"but there is one more thing to your advantage, that I have still to tell you. If you pay cash in advance, there is a further 10 per cent discount." The offer was just too good to refuse, and Mrs Findlay dashed off to the office, returning almost immediately with the cash to secure her advertisement in the journal.

"I'll send on an official receipt when I return to my office on Friday,"said the con-man as he stuffed the poor woman's money into his bulging wallet... "You see I"ve been so busy with this special offer that I've run out of receipts."

After breakfast Whitelaw left the hotel and visited other licensed premises, guest houses and restaurants in the district. Using the same swindling patter, he successfully diddled the various proprietors into parting with their hard-earned cash, on the belief that their businesses were to be advertised in forthcoming issues of 'Rural Scotland.'

After his successful day hood-winking all and sundry, Whitelaw, with great composure, returned to the Harbour Hotel. His brazen attitude aroused no suspicion whatsoever, and again the generous charlatan was back in the lounge bar, buying everyone drinks.

The drinks account was mounting up, but Whitelaw insisted that these be put on his bill. To put everyone's mind at rest, he would occasionally pull out his wallet, for all to see. The sight of the bulging wallet, bursting at the seams with bank notes, had a reassuring effect on Mrs Findlay and her staff.

Mr Whitelaw was obviously going to be able to pay his bill, when the time came. "I'll be leaving tomorrow,Mrs Findlay, so be sure and have my account ready, as it's looking like a busy day ahead for me."

The following morning Mrs Findlay went into the dining room to serve her guests with breakfast, but there was no sign of Whitelaw.

"He's probably slept in," she muttered to herself, as she climbed the stairs to arouse her guest.

When she knocked on his door, it fell open, and poor Mrs Findlay got the shock of her life. Inside the room, there was no sign of Mr Whitelaw. All his luggage was gone! The swindler had gone without settling his bill, which was quite substantial, due to the 'drinks on the house' attitude of Whitelaw in entertaining other patrons in the lounge..

Realising that she had been duped, Mrs Findlay telephoned the police. Detective Inspector Archie Murdoch and Constable Souter went to the hotel and spoke to the unfortunate hotelier, who was very distressed.

The inspector checked the visitors' book, and enquiries revealed that the address given by Whitelaw when he signed in, was a fictitious one. The inspector also contacted the publishers of 'Rural Scotland' magazine, and it came as no great surprise to learn that no one there knew of anyone named Whitelaw, and he certainly was not a company representative.

"Mrs Findlay," said Murdoch, " ah'm awfy sorry tae have tae tell ye that you have been well and truly fleeced. This rogue Whitelaw is an impostor, and certainly has no ties with the firm who publish the Rural Scotland magazine."

The unfortunate Mrs Findlay hadn't even managed to get a description of the car the fraudster was driving. Enquiries at the other businesses only confirmed Inspector Murdoch's suspicions. They too had fallen victims of the smooth-talking swindler.

"He's beaten us," the inspector mumbled to Constable Souter, "He's beaten us. He cruised in here fir a couple o' days, swindled folks oot o' their money, then disappeared withoot trace." The dejected officers returned to the police station.

"He's bamboozled us as well, Souter," groaned Murdoch, who was always a bit downhearted when few or no clues were evident.

"Jist a minute, inspector," gleamed young Souter, "there's wan wee bit that we've overlooked," he continued with an air of elation in his voice.

"Whit's that, Souter," queried the inspector. Souter told his boss how it was just possible that the fraudster had left his calling card, with his full name and address, at the hotel.

Both officers raced to the Harbour Hotel, where they were met by Mrs Findlay and her barmaid. After listening to the inspector, Mrs Findlay said to her barmaid, "Janet, go to the bar and get all those counterfoils for the raffle tickets that we've been selling recently."

The young girl returned with a pile of counterfoils from the raffle ticket books, and the officers frantically fumbled through them. "Here we are, sir," said Souter, holding up a number of ticket counterfoils. "Here are the raffle tickets purchased by Whitelaw."

The conman had stupidly or greedily put down his own name and address on the raffle tickets!

A check at the address shown on the raffle tickets, secured the arrest of the smooth-talking fraudster. Although clever at the art of deception, Whitelaw made the blunder of his lifetime, by writing his proper name and address on the raffle tickets.

The greedy possibility of his winning the holiday in Arran and not being able to claim it was a chance he took.

In an effort to get off with a light sentence, the fraudster told the sheriff that he was due a small inheritance from his Aunt Mabel's estate, and he would be able to repay the money he had misappropriated. The Sheriff sent him to prison for 60 days.

Whitelaw, it transpired, never had an Aunt Mabel!

A GRAVE OFFENCE

A rare, centuries old crime, which still exists, in Scots common law, is "violating sepulchres." This vile offence involves forcibly entering a tomb or grave to steal from the corpse, who sadly by this time, is unable to assist the constabulary in their enquiries.

It is perhaps the lowest and most despicable of all felonies, and one such case did, in fact,take place, much to the horror of everyone, except the culprit.

In Victorian times, it was commonplace for the wealthy and titled to have, on their estate, a private family burial ground. These mausoleums, or ornamental burial grounds, were usually sited in remote, isolated corners and frequently surrounded by trees.

The burial chambers were shallow, and massive heavy stone slabs would cover the tombs, which were sited in a stone building, not unlike a small chapel. There were no doors, just some peaceful old stained glass in the roof and windows. By day, old burial grounds are serene places, and in the city, people gather there at mid-day, and have their packed lunch, without giving a thought to their silent neighbours. But would the same characters venture there alone, on a dark night?

On a cold, bleak December afternoon, Sir James Balmain phoned the local constabulary office, and reported a most disturbing matter, which sent a chill up the spine of police cadet Morgan, who received the call.

Someone had entered the family mausoleum on Sir James's estate and opened one of the tombs.

The startling incident had been discovered by Arthur Gillies, an estate worker, who normally had a red, weather-beaten complexion, but the frightful discovery had turned his face a pale ash colour.

Both he and Sir James were too upset to give a clear account of the matter at this stage, and it was not known if the motive had been theft. There was only a skeleton staff on duty at the station that afternoon, so Constable Fraser and young Cadet Morgan were sent to interview the laird, who was at his mansion house on the estate.

Sir James and Gillies were too overwrought to go near the place. This resulted in Constable Fraser and young Morgan going in on their own, and it was now late afternoon and getting dark. In the fading light they entered the mausoleum, and saw that a massive stone "lid", covering one of the tombs, had been pushed aside, and a partly shrouded corpse was exposed. The atmosphere was chilling and young Morgan, who was just 17, was absolutely petrified.

"Will ye let go o' my hand," belched Fraser, "and gang ootside and see if there's ony footprints or the like." Morgan was relieved to get out of that building! Nothing was found and they returned to the big house and spoke again to Sir James, who was unwilling to go and see if anything had been stolen.

"It was sometimes family custom to bury loved ones and leave a ring or item of jewellery on the body," he said, "but I can't be more specific and would like to assume that, in this instance, nothing has been stolen . If you are finished at the scene, I'll phone Blyth, the undertaker, and get over straight away to put things back in order," he told the officers.

Back at the police station, the officers were discussing the case, over a cup of tea, with Detective Inspector Archie Murdoch and his junior, Constable Soutar. "The only clue, sir," said Fraser, "is that everything at the place is covered with green mould. All the stanes and the stane building itself are mouldy, probably due to the nearby trees. Our uniforms are badly marked with the green mould and ah've tried, unsuccessfully, tae wash it aff," continued Fraser. "What sort o' body would gang along there, in the dead o' night, and dae such a thing,"quipped young Morgan. "Was that supposed tae be funny, Morgan," blurted the Inspector. "Remarks of that nature, could have grave consequences on yer career."

Cases of this nature often prompted light-hearted comments, which were expressed in private, and not intended to offend anyone. It was an acceptable way of releasing the tension and anger everyone felt.

Some weeks passed, and it was the usual Saturday night, when the most common offences seemed to be drink related. Just about an hour after the pubs closed, two constables had arrested James Kemp for being drunk and incapable in the street. Kemp was a burly character in his 30s. His fondness for the demon drink was well known, but it was unusual for him to be in such an incapable state.

Being a forester on the Balmain estate, he was a strong man, and he lived in a small cottage with his wife and family. Being in such an intoxicated state, Kemp was locked up in a cell, for his own safety, until such times as a responsible relative arrived to bail him out.

About two hours later, Mrs Kemp arrived at the police station. Kemp was still very drunk, but his wife assured the duty officer that she would take him straight home."Ah've had an awfy time o' it, the last two weeks wi' him and his drink," she told the officer.

"He's been having nightmares and sleepless nights, but he'll no' tell me whit's wrang." Kemp stood, rather unsteadily, saying nothing, as his release was being arranged..

Prior to being locked up, his personal property, which had only been a small sum of money, had been taken from him. On his release, this was returned,requiring his signature, to acknowledge receipt."He cannae bite his finger, far less sign his name,"said the missus. "I'll sign for him."

By this time, Inspector Murdoch had come into the office, and while Mrs Kemp was leaning on the counter signing the property book, he couldn't help noticing the very fancy-looking ring on her little finger. It looked out of character to see such an expensive-looking ring on the finger of an estate worker's wife.

"That's a braw ring," said a curious Archie. "Could ah get a wee look at it?" "Certainly," she said, removing the ring from her finger, and handing it over. "This drunken man o' mine gave me it two weeks ago."

The inspector saw that it was a fine looking emerald-and-diamond ring, which bore an inscription on the inside. Using his magnifying glass, Archie saw the inscription 'TO GB 1887.' Could this be Gertrude Balmain, aunt of Sir James, he thought.

"I'm afraid I'll have to keep this ring, and yer husband meantime," said the inspector..... "His bail is cancelled,"he remarked, "and tell me, Mrs Kemp, where did he get the ring?" "Ah'm saying no more Mr Murdoch," came the reply.

In the eyes of the law, a wife cannot be compelled to give evidence against her spouse, so Archie did not pursue the conversation with Mrs Kemp. Her husband was returned to the cells to sober up, after which he would be questioned by Inspector Murdoch. In the interval, the inspector obtained a search warrant to go over Kemp's cottage.

"But what will ye be looking fir,Archie," queried the station sergeant. "I'll be looking for clothing that is stained with thick green moss," came the reply.

At the cottage, Mrs Kemp said,"There's nae need tae turn the place upside doon, officer, because there's a jaiket and pair of

44

troosers lying below the sink. I've been trying fir twa weeks tae get thae green marks oot."

The inspector knew he had Kemp's presence at the mausoleum beyond doubt, but he still had to get Sir James to identify the ring, and this was not going to be easy, as the laird was not aware of anything being stolen.

"I'm sorry to call on you at this unearthly hour, Sir James, but a matter of some urgency has cropped up."At the same time he showed the ring taken from Mrs Kemp. "Is there any chance that this may have come from the finger of your deceased aunt Gertrude?" Sir James thought it possible, but he could not be sure. Suddenly he remembered that in the attic there was an old family photograph of aunt Gertrude, and he soon found it. It was a large photograph of the lady, and on her finger, the very distinctive ring could be clearly seen.

Inspector Murdoch took possession of the photograph, and on his return to the police station, the suspect Kemp had sobered up sufficiently to be interviewed.

When confronted with the ring, the mould stained clothing, and the photograph of the deceased lady, Kemp broke down and confessed to breaking into the tomb and removing the ring from the corpse.

He offered no explanation and was adamant that he alone had moved the heavy stone slab covering the tomb. Having had nightmares since, he resorted to drink, and was now greatly relieved to get the matter off his chest.

Some months later, while her husband was in jail for his heinous crime,Mrs Kemp called on Archie Murdoch, and showed him an old magazine she had come across in the cottage. One of the reports in the magazine referred to the discovery of many valuables, which had lain for centuries in the tombs in Egypt." "I wonder if this is where he got the daft idea from,"she said.

THE OTHER BILL THOMSON

Down at the railway station Bill Thomson was employed as a goods clerk by the railway company. His office formed part of the old fashioned railway station and was quaint in character, with its Victorian furnishings, mahogany desks, counters, large high stools in front of writing slopes,and the gentle ticking of the round wood-framed wall clock which seems to be a hallmark of all railway property. Mr Thomson's duties were mainly clerical and he looked after the business of goods, parcels and packages in transit on the railway network.

It was a very hot July afternoon and the clerk sat sweating profusely in front of one of the big writing slopes on the public counter. He looked out into the car park and saw a strange man get out of a small blue van, and remove a large brown suitcase from the rear of the vehicle. After fiddling about for some time the mystery figure walked towards the goods office carrying the suitcase."Here's an odd character heading our way," Bill said to his colleague, Derek Lamont, who was also peering out of the office window."What on earth is he doing wearing a great big heavy overcoat on a scorching day like this?"queried Derek. At this point the man came into the office and thrust the suitcase on to the counter in front of the baffled clerks. "I would like this delivered tae Edinburgh on the next available train," the stranger said

The clerks had a procedure where they made out special address labels and attached them to the parcels in transit. When he asked the relative details Bill was taken aback when the man gave the name and address for delivery of the package. "Bill Thomson, 3 Barton Mews, Edinburgh,"replied the man quietly. By strange coincidence the name was the same as that of the railway clerk. "Fine warm day," the clerk casually commented, whilst curiously glancing at the heavy overcoat worn by the customer..

The sinister man did not respond and left quietly after paying the delivery charge. The matter was soon forgotten and, apart from the man's attire, there was nothing else odd about the transaction. Two weeks later the railway clerk sat at his desk, gazing out of the office window, when a small blue van came into the car park. It was being driven by the same man and, as before, he wore a very heavy

46

overcoat despite it again being a hot day.

As before, the stranger brought a brown heavy suitcase into the office and requested it be delivered to the same Edinburgh address. When making payment for the transaction the man fiddled about with his wallet, eventually producing some money to meet the cost. Seconds after the man left the office, the clerk noticed that a card lay on the floor and appeared to have fallen from the man's wallet. Bill Thomson noticed that it was a business card in the name of "Bill Thomson,3 Barton Mews, Edinburgh."

The clerk ran to the nearby car park and handed the property over to the stranger who was just about to drive off in his van. "Thank you," the man said quietly,"Its my business card." He then drove off. Returning to his office Bill commented to his colleague,"Why on earth should the man be sending parcels tae himself? Surely it would be just as easy taking the stuff home with him in his van."

Later in the day Police Constable Fraser called at the goods office where a cup of tea was always available, and he would pass the time engaged in idle conversation with the staff. It was not long before Bill Thomson was relating the strange encounter with the man in the heavy overcoat.. "Could you mind his name?" queried the Constable. "No bother," came the reply. "His name is exactly the same as my own," but the clerk had to refer to the office delivery invoice to furnish the address. The Constable had no definite reason to suspect anything untoward at the time and no further action was taken.

Several days passed by and Constable Fraser was on duty at the police office when he received a telephone message from police in Edinburgh about a matter concerning something totally different. At the end of the enquiry Constable Fraser asked his Edinburgh colleague if he knew anything of a "Bill Thomson". "Most definitely," came the reply. "Thomson is a well-known shoplifter, and he uses the same method of stealing goods, despite being caught red-handed on a number of occasions." The officer described how the suspect, in all weathers, would wear a large overcoat to conceal goods when he went into a shop stealing. He would then post the goods on to himself, thereby reducing the chance of being caught in possession, should his van be stopped and searched by the police."But here is the interesting bit," continued the Edinburgh officer."We have a warrant for Thomson's arrest. He's wanted for attempted murder."

Apparently some time back Thomson was detained by a store detective who had observed him shoplifting. A struggle ensued and

Thomson pulled a knife and repeatedly stabbed the poor man, before making good his escape. The address last used by Thomson was checked but, as on previous occasions, the suspect had vanished. He was in the habit of using an address for just a short time, and was obviously trying to keep one step ahead of the police. The enquiries switched back to Constable Fraser's area, and it was believed that at this time, Thomson was not aware that the police were on his trail.

Detective Inspector Archie Murdoch suspected that the villain, although having a fresh address, would still use the local railway station to despatch his ill-gotten goods."If he's still shoplifting in our area we'll soon pick him up,"commented Murdoch. It was decided that, due to the gravity of the crime of attempted murder, observation be kept at the goods office. Constable Fraser and Cadet Morgan were instructed by the inspector to change from their uniform into plain clothes, as it had been arranged for them to work as temporary goods clerks at the railway station. The undercover officers patiently spent the first weeks of the surveillance doing nothing but drinking endless cups of tea and blethering. There was no trace of the suspect, and the enquiry was to be stood down at the end of the week, unless something of great interest cropped up. On the very last day the breakthrough came.

Constable Fraser and Cadet Morgan, dressed in their plain clothes, were seated at a desk in the goods office when suddenly one of the railway clerks announced,"Here he comes." The clerk pointed to the car park where the suspect was removing a big suitcase from his van. Fraser quickly phoned the police station for assistance. After all the quiet suspect was a man who had previously become extremely violent and dangerous when cornered, and who knew how he would react when confronted? The mystery man came into the goods office and put the case on the counter, requesting that it be delivered to an address quite different from the one he had previously used, although he continued to employ the name Bill Thomson. Playing for time, the two officers discreetly made their way to the public side of the counter and stood beside the unsuspecting villain. Nervously and impatiently glancing out of the window, waiting for his colleagues to arrive, Constable Fraser decided he could hold off no longer. "Mr Thomson," said Fraser,"we are police officers," and before he could finish the suspect dashed towards the door. Cadet Morgan, who had been a full back in the high school rugby team, brought the fleeing escapee down with a flying tackle, and after some scuffling the rogue was handcuffed, and his detention secured. While the officers and suspect lay struggling on the floor, Inspector Murdoch came into the office, and took charge. Realising the game was well and truly up, the suspect resisted no further. His suitcase was searched and found to contain a varied amount of goods, which he had stolen earlier from local shops. Inspector Murdoch congratulated his officers and commended them for the brave way they handled a most dangerous man. The risk the officers had taken was even more frightening, when the suspect was searched. In his coat pocket, Inspector Murdoch discovered that the villain was in possession of a large sheath knife!

Bill Thomson, the criminal, was taken to Edinburgh and handed over to the police there, pending the more serious charge of stabbing the store detective. Bill Thomson, the railway goods clerk, will never forget his encounter with his namesake!

SURGEON SEALS CASE

Gazing down at the lifeless body of a wee boy, Detective Inspector Murdoch, his face etched with anger and disbelief, gasped,"How on earth can someone do this to a bairn?"

Other officers at the murder scene were equally angered and shocked at the discovery of Jamie Ross, an eight-year-old schoolboy, who had been reported missing by his distraught mother some hours earlier.

Jamie's body lay on the grass in a clearing amongst some whin bushes, which bordered a path on the golf course. The pathway was very popular with cyclists and walkers.

"Surely someone will have seen something here," said the inspector while he pondered on how best to proceed with the inquiry into the most foul of all crimes. "The only witness we have so far is young Billy Ellis, who discovered the body," said Detective Sergeant Lindsay."About an hour ago Ellis was cycling along the path when he heard moans, and on going into the whins, he found young Jamie."

The police surgeon arrived at the scene and pronounced life extinct. The victim had been savagely beaten. "The weapon could have been a stick or even a golf club," remarked Mr Sutherland, the surgeon. The officers at the scene were numbed by the tragic discovery, and they knew what was coming next. It was a duty no one wanted to perform.

"Someone will have to notify the boy's mither", said Murdoch, looking for a volunteer. The arduous, painful task fell on Sergeant McPherson, and it was perhaps the most terrible moment in his career, when he broke the shocking news to Mrs. Ross.

It was also necessary for the poor woman to attend at the scene and formally identify her son. This heartbreaking task was duly done with the help of good neighbours, who comforted Mrs. Ross as best they could, in the terrible circumstances.

The formalities were done, and the child's body was removed to the mortuary for further examination. An immediate post-mortem confirmed that the child had died as a result of a severe blow to the skull with a blunt instrument. The weapon, if found, would surely have traces of the boy's blood and hair adhering to it.

"It's imperative that we find this weapon quickly," commented

Inspector Murdoch as he detailed a group of officers to search the immediate area where the body was found."In the meantime, Sergeant Lindsay and I will speak tae the lad who found the body."

It is unfortunate, but necessary, in all cases of murder, to suspect the person who makes the grim discovery. "Until such times that I can eliminate him from our enquiry, Billy Ellis is the main suspect," remarked Murdoch.

Because Ellis was just 15, the officers had to interview the juvenile in the presence of his father, at the police station.

"Now, Billy, tell me exactly what happened," asked Murdoch. The boy repeated his earlier account that he had been cycling along the golf course path, when he heard moaning and groaning coming from the bushes. He went into the dense whins and found the injured boy.

"Was he still moaning at this time?" queried Inspector Murdoch. "Yes," came the reply, "but I just left him and ran for help " continued Ellis. Inspector Murdoch was uneasy. He knew that forensic evidence was of little value as far as Ellis was concerned. After all, he had been at the scene discovering the body, so it was obvious that traces of his presence there would be found.

Ellis even admitted touching the body, so any traces of blood on his person could be reasonably explained. Two hours had passed since Ellis had discovered the body of Jamie Ross. The interview with the lad was interrupted when Constable Fraser came into the room with dramatic news for Inspector Murdoch.

"The pathologist is adamant that young Jamie was dead for at least eight hours," Fraser whispered into the inspector's ear, "so there's no way that Ellis could have found the boy alive two hours ago!"

Inspector Murdoch now had firm suspicions about Billy Ellis. His tone of voice changed. He became severe and uncompromising as he angrily questioned the suspect. "There is no way you could have heard Jamie moaning, either before or after your discovery," he sternly remarked.

Billy Ellis, though just 15, stuck to his story and insisted that his account was correct. The inspector sensed that, although Ellis was a juvenile, he was cunning and hesitant before answering any questions. While all this was going on, other officers were making enquiries elsewhere and conducting a detailed search of the area where Jamie was found.

It was learned that Jamie had gone along by the golf course to search for golf balls. Lots of the local children would do this, and sell the balls back to the golfers. Jamie had spoken to two other boys that day and he had shown them a ball he had found. The boys recalled that the name 'Royal Insurance' was stamped on the ball, and this was later found to be unusual. Meanwhile the clearing where the body was found was searched.

Directly underneath where the body had lain, officers found a small brass ringlet, and a tiny curved piece of black and red plastic, about the size of a fingernail. These two tiny fragments were vital because they had been below the body. The report of the finding of these items was passed on to Inspector Murdoch, who, for the time being, had suspended the interview with Billy Ellis.

Enquiries soon established that the brass eyelet was from a shoe, and the small bit of plastic was identical to that found on golf clubs, where the shaft and the head of the club are joined. To conceal the join, a small tubular piece of black and red plastic is placed around that part of the club. Inspector Murdoch and Sergeant Lindsay returned to the interview room to resume questioning Billy Ellis.

The suspect's shoes were removed for examination. On the left shoe, there was nothing untoward. Twelve brass eyelets through which the laces were threaded were intact, but the right shoe really swung the enquiry into a new dimension! On this shoe, one of the eyelets was missing, and the others matched perfectly the one found at the scene. "That's no unusual," protested the suspect, "after all, I did find the wee boy."

"Yes," said Murdoch, "but if you had lost that wee brass ring from your shoe, it would have been found beside the body, and not underneath it."

"Do you have a set of golf clubs?" continued the inspector with his questioning. At this point, Ellis's father spoke up. "He uses my clubs from time to time." "Well, I'll have to send an officer round to your house to pick up the golf clubs for examination," continued the inspector, who also reminded Mr. Ellis that he could obtain a warrant for this purpose, if he were unwilling to co-operate.

The clubs were brought back to the police station, where examination revealed the most damning of evidence. Missing from the mashie-niblick was a small piece of the hose plastic. When the recovered piece was compared, it fitted perfectly into place. The jagged edges matched the club exactly. It was now obvious to the officers that Billy Ellis had attacked the boy and struck him with this golf club.

In the struggle he lost the eyelet from his shoe, and the fragment from the club, before the poor victim fell on top of the items.

Forensic examination of the club later revealed tiny traces of blood and hair, which matched those of the victim.

When confronted with the new evidence, Billy Ellis broke down and cried, confessing to the vile crime. Apparently he had been cycling along, with his golf clubs on his back, and accidentally collided with the wee boy, and fell to the ground. This caused a violent, angry reaction and he struck the child with a golf club.

In an uncontrollable burst of anger, Billy Ellis went too far, and before he regained control, he had inflicted the most horrendous and fatal injuries to the poor boy. Some hours later, in an attempt to conceal his actions, Ellis made up the story of finding the boy.

The strange thing was that the golf ball, bearing the name 'Royal Insurance' was never found, despite Jamie Ross having had it in his possession when he was last seen alive.

"You know," said Sergeant Lindsay, "we always tell bairns not to talk to strangers, but in my experience, the majority of attacks on children are committed by people they know."

NOT ALWAYS EVIDENT!

In their younger days Geordie Steedman and his wife,Hilda, had long been suspected of crimes of dishonesty, such as theft by shoplifting, fraud and the like. Despite being the subject of a number of police enquiries this husband and wife team were never actually convicted of any crime.

This annoyed Inspector Archie Murdoch and he always had the impression that Steedman badgered and bullied his wife to support his dishonest activities. But that was years ago, and the Steedmans had more or less retired into a quiet life and avoided the attention of the police.

One morning old Geordie sat at the breakfast table staring at a bowl of porridge, which had just been put in front of him by his long suffering wife.

"There's nae saut in this parritch," he roared at the poor woman.

"Eat it up ye crabbit auld devil," replied Mrs Steedman. "It'll no dae ye any harm tae take it wance withoot salt."

Muttering and moaning Geordie devoured the oats, stood up from the table, then promptly dropped down dead on the kitchen floor! His panic stricken wife phoned the doctor but it was all too late. Geordie Steedman had had his last bowl of porridge, and the doctor pronounced life extinct.

"I'm afraid in cases of sudden death I am obliged to notify the police," said Dr Carson to the widow.

"Surely nae salt in his porridge widnae kill him doctor,"gasped the distraught and bewildered woman.

"No,no," replied the doctor,"mair than likely too much salt during his lifetime,brought on what looks like a stroke to me."

The police were duly summoned and Constables Fraser and Wilson were soon at the scene of this sudden and unfortunate death. Addressing the upset widow, PC Fraser sympathetically said,'We'll need tae get particulars from his birth certificate in order that a report can be prepared fir the fiscal."

Due to her distressed state the woman was unable to cope and she invited the officers to rifle through a chest of drawers where the sought after document might be found. Constable Fraser searched the cabinet and soon found the birth certificate of the now departed George Steedman.

The deceased's body was removed to the mortuary for a post mortem, and on completion of the formalities, the officers returned to the police station to make out their report for the fiscal.

The officers retired to the police canteen where a number of other officers, including Detective Inspector Murdoch and Sergeant MacPherson, were having their tea break.

"Is this just a straightforward sudden death?" queried Sergeant MacPherson

"Aye," replied Constable Wilson,"but there is something bothering me now, and ah think Inspector Murdoch will no be very amused when ah tell him whit happened."

Murdoch spluttered over his mug of tea when he heard this remark. "Whit do ye mean?" gasped the inspector.

The young constable looked perplexed and unsure of himself.

"Ah jist dinna ken whaur tae start,and at the end o' the day yer gonna be rappin' ma knuckles fir no' takin' ony action," said Wilson.

By this time the atmosphere in the canteen was one of complete silence as young Wilson explained.

"When the upset Mrs Steedman invited me tae search fir her late man's birth certificate, she either suffered a temporary lapse o' memory, or she had nae idea whit was in the drawers."

"Whit dae ye mean Wilson?" queried Inspector Murdoch,with a most impatient tone of voice.

"Well apart from the birth certificate, the drawers were packed with jewellery, gold rings, watches, necklaces and the like."

The inexperienced constable went on to say that he had not sought any explanation from the widow, regarding this cache of valuables.

"It wis a delicate moment, Inspector," muttered Wilson,"Efter a' the poor woman had jist lost her husband so ah couldnae very weel put her through the third degree."

"Hoo no?" said young Cadet Morgan who just happened to be eavesdropping.

Inspector Murdoch now assumed control. "Ah've long suspected that Steedman wis a fence(receiver of stolen goods) and ah'm willing tae bet that all that jewellery is from a number of break-ins we've investigated recently."

There had been a string of posh houses in the district where burglaries had occurred and jewellery been stolen. The police had solved some of these crimes, but the culprits involved had refused point blank to divulge where they had disposed of the property.

"It'll hae been Steedman all along who's been buying up all this stuff and we've never known aboot it,"commented Murdoch.

"We could hardly go along there at this time wi' a search warrant,"said Sergeant MacPherson,"the poor woman will be in some state at the loss of her man."

"We'll wait a few days," said Murdoch."After all we have a duty tae recover stolen property and return it tae the rightful owners."

"But the insurance companies will have compensated those victims," said Sergeant MacPherson, who still seemed reluctant to take any action,"and in ony case we cannae charge a dead man wi' reset."

"Aye that's true sergeant," replied Murdoch,"but some o' that jewellery will have great sentimental value,and such items cannot be replaced by insurance."

A few days later, armed with a search warrant, the CID officers and Constable Wilson returned to the Steedman home.

When confronted by the officers, the widow surprised everyone with her calm, composed and understanding attitude.

"Poor woman, it must be the bereavement," the inspector thought to himself, as he explained to her what Wilson had noticed earlier, when searching for the birth certificate.

"There must be some mistake inspector," said Mrs Steedman with a wry smirk on her face. "The constable must have had delusions, or been indulging in strong alcohol."

The officers were then ushered to the chest of drawers where Wilson had previously observed the jewellery.

"See fir yersel', there's nothing o' that like there,"she claimed.

Sure enough when Murdoch searched the chest, nothing of any interest was found. The newspaper-lined drawers just contained old papers, clothing and bits and pieces. The Inspector scowled at young Wilson, seeking some sort of explanation for this awkward and embarrassing situation. At the same time Murdoch grovelled and apologised to the widow for causing her so much upset,especially at this difficult time.

"No need tae worry, inspector, yer jist doin' yer job," she responded,again with an odd smile on her face. The sort of smile that says,"I know something you don't know."

"Ah dinnae suppose ye'll be feeling like offering us a cup o' tea," said Wilson in his usual tactless manner. The whole enquiry was an absolute fiasco and Murdoch was left feeling very uneasy at the outcome.

"Had ye been drinking at all?" he jokingly asked Wilson. "Not at all , sir, certainly not," came the indignant reply.

Referring to Mrs.Steedman, and attempting to console the young constable, Murdoch said, "The auld besom beat us to it. She realised her blunder in inviting ye tae search the chest, then when it dawned on her that ye had seen the jewellery, she got rid o' it before we returned."

"Hoo dae ye ken that, sir?" asked Wilson.

"Did ye no' notice that the bottom o' the drawers were lined wi' newspapers?" replied the inspector.

"Aye, but whit has that got tae dae wi' it?"

"Well," said Murdoch, with a smug look on his face, "Ah noticed the date o' the newspaper covering the bottom o' the drawers."

"Whit's significant aboot that?" quizzed Wilson.

"The date on the newsprint was the day after her man died. She obviously cleaned oot the chest, after you left and before we returned wi' the search warrant!"

It seemed that yet again, the Steedmans had avoided the police and escaped justice.

"Ah'll catch her wan o' thae days," vowed Murdoch.

A CLOSE SHAVE

It was about 7.30 in the morning when Detective Inspector Archie Murdoch was driving down the High Street in the unmarked car used by CID personnel.

The place was very quiet with the shops not due to open for at least another hour. The calm was soon interrupted when Murdoch saw two burly uniformed policemen chasing a man down the street. The odd man wore only a pair of trousers, a vest and a pair of sandshoes, and, by the way he was distancing himself from the policemen, he was obviously quite fit. Or perhaps the policemen were unfit!

Both officers were portly and overweight, and trying to run in this state, while wearing heavy police uniforms, was not easy. The inspector was about to intervene, when the running man, in the vest, disappeared down a close, followed some distance behind by the constables. Murdoch knew the close well.

The lane ran between the High Street and Sea Road, and it started between two shops, then was bordered on both sides by a very high stone wall. All the inspector had to do was drive round to the close exit in Sea Road, and wait for the pursuing officers to chase the man into his arms.

Murdoch was quickly in position, and as he waited at the foot of the close, he could hear running footsteps. Suddenly a figure emerged from the lane. "Gotcha," shouted Murdoch as he grabbed the man, who was breathless and offered no resistance. Shortly after, the two exhausted policemen "breezed" from the close gasping for air.

"Calm down lad," said the inspector, holding on to the man he detained. Both officers looked dismayed and flabbergasted, but were unable to speak until they got their breath back.

"There's jist wan thing wrong, inspector," gasped Constable Irvine as he stared quizzically at the suspect: "The man we chased into the close was wearing a vest and sandshoes. This chap you've detained is wearing a tweed jacket, a bonnet and ordinary shoes!"

Archie stepped back in disbelief. Sure enough the man who ran into the close was not the man who ran out of it! "What the heck is your game? " the inspector angrily asked the wee timid man in the tweed jacket.

"I was walking up the close, when I saw these two big figures running towards me, and I don't know why, but I just turned on ma heels and ran," said the detained man. He went on to explain that he had gotten a fright, and as the officers' hats had earlier fallen off in the chase, he had not recognised them as policemen.

By failing to spot that the man who emerged from the close was quite differently dressed from the man who ran into it, Inspector Murdoch's pride was severely dented, and all he could do was apologise to the poor wee fellow he had detained.

"Did ye no see a man running doon the close wearing a vest and sandshoes?" queried Murdoch. "No. The only people I seen, turncd out tae be thae twa big policemen," came the reply.

The officers were baffled and stood scratching their heads wondering what to do next. "There's no way out of that close," said Constable Irvine, "other than on to Sea Road here, and the walls are that high it would be impossible for a man to climb over," he continued.

All three officers went back up the High Street, but the sinister man in the vest had vanished into thin air. There were quite a number of closes running from High Street down to Sea Road, and there were no exits where a person could disappear. Once in the close, the only way out was at Sea Road.

The baffled officers stood in the High Street roughly where the suspect was last seen. "What actually happened?" Inspector Murdoch asked the constables. "We were simply walking along High Street, when we saw the man nearby," replied Constable Irvine, "and when he saw us, he just turned on his heels and ran, so we gave chase."

"Then you came on the scene, Inspector," said the other officer, "and the man ran down the close at the side of the cinema there."

The constable pointed to the close. "But wait a minute," said Murdoch, "the boy on the vest never ran intae that close. It was the next one he ran into," continued the inspector, pointing to a close just 20 yards away from the cinema close.

"Yer a right pair of donkeys," blasted Murdoch, "You've ran intae the wrang close." The two lanes in question merged into one at the Sea Road end, and it now appeared that the vest-clad man had done a 'U' turn, when he realised that he was no longer being pursued.

In the meantime, the man in the tweed jacket was given an apology and allowed to go on his way.

Murdoch and the two policemen returned to the police station. "You'll be the laughing stock of the station," he told the officers, "and you'll have tae file a report on the incident for future reference." Later that day, Inspector Murdoch was due in court, and he was being given a lift there in a police car driven by Sergeant Wilson, with young Cadet Morgan in the passenger seat.

As the police vehicle travelled down Mill Road, a man wearing trousers, vest and sandshoes was standing on the footpath. "That's the man I've been telling you about," screamed Murdoch.

Sergeant Wilson stopped the car, and he and Cadet Morgan got out. On seeing the police, the man turned on his heels and ran off, with Sergeant Wilson and Cadet Morgan chasing after him. On this occasion, however, the fleeing man was out of luck, because Cadet Morgan was a keen young sprinter, and he soon caught up with the fugitive. The peculiar suspect was detained and brought back to the police vehicle.

Later enquiries revealed that the 'sprinting' suspect was a person who was mentally ill and of unsound mind. Other officers knew of his past, and it transpired that he derived some sort of pleasure by giving the police the run-around.

Some days later, back at the police station, Detective Inspector Murdoch was sitting at his desk, when Constable Irvine came in and placed the current edition of Police Gazette on the inspector's desk.

The Gazette is circulated nationwide to all police stations, and gives details of persons wanted for crimes committed in other force areas. Pointing to a picture in the Gazette of a suspect wanted for a series of frauds in Edinburgh, Constable Irvine asked the inspector, "Do ye recognise this man, Sir?" Murdoch stared in disbelief at the photograph of the wanted man.

It was, without doubt, the man in the tweed jacket and bonnet, who had been 'mistakenly' detained by Murdoch, as he ran out of the High Street close, with the constables in hot pursuit. "The first person tae say anything aboot this will be on traffic duty fir a year," blasted an embarrassed Inspector Murdoch, as he banged his fist on the desk and failed to notice the drawing pin he had left there only a few moments earlier.

The rest of the officers knew from experience that if ever there was a time to remain silent this was it. The fraudster Inspector Murdoch had detained, then apologised to, was never seen again.

For the criminal it had, indeed, been "a close shave."

BOWLER'S NIGHTMARE

One evening in September, members of the local bowling club were gathered in the club house for the annual general meeting when the chairman, Bill Donaldson, announced, "Can I have your attention, ladies and gentlemen. I'm afraid our treasurer, Charlie Mitchell, hasn't yet arrived, so the meeting will not now commence until eight."

Charlie Mitchell was normally a most reliable and punctual man. He was quite elderly, and lived alone in a cottage not far from the green.

"Perhaps he's got the dates mixed up, or lost track of time," said the chairman, as he despatched two of the members to call round at Charlie's house, and find out if anything was amiss.

The members soon reported back that the cottage was in total darkness, and their repeated knocking on the door had received no response.

It was now long after eight o'clock, and the treasurer's absence resulted in the meeting being postponed for that evening.

Later that night, the same two members returned to the cottage, and they became quite anxious when their repeated efforts to arouse Mitchell failed. Their concern for his well-being increased when they noticed that the early morning delivery of milk was still on the doorstep. Fearing that something had befallen Charlie, the police were summoned and Constables Fraser and Robertson were quickly on the scene.

The officers forced open the front door of the cottage, and their worst fears were realised. In the living room they found the pitiful body of Charlie Mitchell slumped in an armchair. On a small table beside the lifeless soul, the officers found an empty pill bottle, and a note written by Mitchell, clearly indicating that he had taken his own life. But this was no ordinary suicide note. It contained something of a more sinister tone.

In his final letter, Mitchell admitted many debts, most of which had been incurred by gambling, and the pitiable treasurer had used up all the bowling club money. Having mis-appropriated the funds for his own gain, he could not face the humiliation of it all, once the matter became public knowledge. It was, however, the second part

61

of the note which resulted in Detective Inspector Archie Murdoch and Detective Sergeant Lindsay being summoned to the scene.

In accordance with procedure, the police doctor also attended to pronounce life extinct. This sad occurrence was undoubtedly a straight forward suicide, but what kindled the inspector's curiosity was the last paragraph in Charlie Mitchell's final letter.

The closing chapter of the puzzling suicide note read, "I can't face the shame of what I' ve done, but if you ask Donaldson, our chairman, what he was getting up to on the 10th of June, you'll uncover something much worse. He knew I was fiddling the cash, and warned me to stay quiet about what happened, or he would tell the police, and I would go to jail."

This sinister allegation against Bill Donaldson gave no further details, and left Inspector Murdoch with a daunting task. "Ah wish Mitchell had been mair specific about what happened on the 10th of June. He's telling us that Donaldson got up to something, but what did he do, and whaur did he dae it," said Murdoch in his usual muttering tone.

Staring at the now departed Charlie Mitchell slumped in the armchair, Sergeant Lindsay replied, "Well, there's wan thing for sure, Archie, he's no going tae tell us noo!"

Back at the police station, it was decided that very discreet enquiries be made concerning the bowling club chairman. A check of the local police records failed to reveal anything untoward or unusual having occurred on June the 10th, as cited in the fateful letter. At this juncture, the officers were reluctant to simply approach Donaldson and seek an explanation, or ask him to account for his movements on the day in question.

What was quickly established though was the fact that since about June, Donaldson had been seen to be drinking heavily by other bowling club members. His wife had died early in the year, and everyone assumed that the chairman was having difficulty living alone, and coping with the stress of his great loss.

His moods, character and conduct were expected, because he and his late wife, although retired, were very close and both active members of the bowling club.During discreet enquiries, it was also learned that Donaldson had not driven his car of late.

He simply dismissed any comments by stating that the old vehicle had mechanical defects and was locked away, because it was no longer roadworthy.

The inspector felt that the unravelling of this mystery lay at the bowling club, and it was there that enquiries were focused. It was learned that on June 10th, bowling club members had travelled to the neighbouring county to play in a league match. These outings were notable social occasions, and following the bowling everyone gathered in the clubhouse for tea, and it was also commonplace for some members to consume a fair measure of alcohol.

The immediate question in Inspector's Murdoch's mind was, "Had Donaldson and Mitchell taken part, and had they perhaps travelled together?" The answer to both questions was in the affirmative, and the match records even confirmed that the two men had partnered each other in the doubles match.

Inspector Murdoch travelled to Perthshire to question members of the host club, and a number of members recalled that, on the evening in question, Donaldson had consumed a fair amount of alcohol, and they were quite concerned about his ability to drive back home. As often is the case, Donaldson declared himself fit to drive, and he and Charlie Mitchell left together.

"How can you be sure it was June 10th?" Murdoch asked one of the members. "Because that evening, a laddie on a bike was knocked down and killed by a hit and run driver. It was in a' the local papers," was the chilling reply.

Because Murdoch was in a neighbouring county, he quickly realised that press reports in his own area may well have not covered this story. At the time, the informant had not suspected that Donaldson could have been responsible for this hit and run accident. Murdoch carried on his probe, and learned that the young boy was riding a red bicycle when he was struck by a car, which had failed to stop.

Officers at the time discovered traces of blue paint at the scene, and part of a broken headlamp, which had come from a Morris car.

Efforts to trace this vehicle had failed. Inspector Murdoch now had sufficient information to justify taking Donaldson into custody during enquiries.

Murdoch and Sergeant Lindsay called at Donaldson's house, and found him in a state of intoxication, so it was arranged for other officers to take the suspect to the police station, where he would be questioned when he sobered up.

In the interval, the CID officers searched Donaldson's house and lock-up garage, where they found a blue Morris car. Close inspection of the vehicle revealed traces of red paint on the front bumper and bonnet, which were later examined by forensic experts, and confirmed to have come from the poor boy's bicycle.

The front headlamp of the vehicle was also broken, and this matched up with the fragments found at the scene.

Donaldson was a broken man. He seemed relieved that his nightmare was over, and he further admitted that he had blackmailed his passenger, Charlie Mitchell, to stay silent after the incident. To further this means, he had known that Charlie had fiddled the bowling club cash, and used this knowledge to secure his silence.

For Charlie Mitchell, the nightmare was over, but for Donaldson, he will have to live with his wretched conscience until the day he dies. Had he stopped, following the accident, and summoned medical help, the unfortunate young victim might have survived, instead of being left alone to die in a country lane on the summer evening of June 10th.